Holy Smoke:
Trapped by Hellfire

A screenplay by:
Russ Brandon

Registered WGA 166329 Copyright Russ Brandon 1998.

Print ISBN: 978-1-7346364-5-1
Ebook ISBN: 978-1-7346364-4-4

Library of Congress Control Number: 2021909522

Cover Design by Teresa Dilley.
Map by Barna Ban.

For any interest in this script, for more information, or to schedule a book club or book store event, contact Russ at *holysmoketrappedbyhellfire@gmail.com.*

You can also visit me on Facebook at:
https://www.facebook.com/Holy-Smoke-Trapped-by-Hellfire-106190278307189

To my dad, who never finished his book.
To all those who helped, to my family,
above all my wife... thanks.

In memory of Patrick David, 24,
killed in the fires of 1988.

"My Drops of Tears I'll Turn to Sparks of Fire"

—William Shakespeare

INTRODUCTION TO SCREENPLAYS

Have you ever read a movie script? If not, here's all you need to know on how writers format screenplays.

I.   Each scene begins with a heading or slug line, written in all capital letters. It tells the reader three things; whether the scene takes place inside, abbreviated as INT. for INTERIOR or inside, where the scene is located, and the time of day. Scene headings use EXT., abbreviated as EXT. for EXTERIOR.

II.   After the scene heading is a brief descriptions to set the scene for characters, setting and action. They are written as text blocks usually around four lines. Note, the first time the writer introduces a character, their character name is in all capital letters, followed by a few words of description.

III. Dialogue is written in a fashion that is similar to a stage play. The character speaking is in all caps with the dialogue. A parenthetical is used to describe the character's action or emotion when they deliver the dialogue.

IV.   Action sequences come in small blocks of text and are not indented.

V.   Any important sounds or visuals are either in all CAPS, *italicized*, or <u>underlined</u> to emphasize them.

VI.   A (V.O.) or voice over, is placed after a character's name in dialogue and means that you hear their voice but they are not physically at that scene location. An (O.S.) is off screen. A character speaking off-screen is at that scene's location, but you can't see them.

VII. Flashbacks and dream sequences are announced in all caps.

Some of the best stories of my generation were written down as screenplays. They are different from books because they are meant to be read easily and so that you can picture the story. This is your chance to cast the characters, put them in costumes, give them voices and set them about action sequences.

Cast of Characters

Fire Lookout One .... *Sheridan Fire Tower Lookout*

Vicky Iglesias .... *Yellowstone Park Ranger and Ph.D. Candidate*

Scruffy .... *Vicky's Dog*

Dr. Bullock .... *Vicky's Dissertation Advisor*

John Duka .... *Yellowstone Park Superintendent*

Cody .... *Yellowstone Park Deputy Superintendent*

Lily .... *Yellowstone Park Fire Behavior Specialist*

Fire Lookout Two .... *Red Fire Tower Lookout*

Fire Lookout Three .... *Shoshone Fire Tower Lookout*

Patrick .... *Yellowstone Park Ranger and Smokejumper*

Sal .... *Young New York City Lawyer*

Cornelius .... *Young Park Visitor*

Keezheekoni .... *Indigenous Park Ranger*

Child .... *Park Visitor*

Pioneer .... *Park Bum and Vietnam Vet*

Maria .... *Pregnant Wife of Patrick*

Ann Maranek .... *Local TV Reporter*

Fire Fighter One and Two...................... *Firefighters on Keezkoni's Crew*

Michael .... *Helicopter Pilot*

Matt and Christine .... *Patrick's Parents*

Pipeman .... *Firefighter on Keezkoni's Crew*

Jefferson .... *Lead Smokejumper*

Red .... *Smokejumper on Patrick's Crew*

Radio Operator .... *Firefighter on Keezkoni's Crew*

Firefighting HQ .... *Firefighting Operations Radio Operator*

Smokejumper One .... *Smokejumper on Patrick's Crew*

Missoula Airport Dispatcher .... *Missoula Airport Control Tower*

EMT .... *Emergency Medical Technician*

Captain .... *Pioneer's Platoon Captain in Vietnam*

Young Woman and two small children .... *Vietnamese POWs*

Kendall .... *United States Secretary of the Interior*

Dr. Young .... *Emergency Hospital Tent Doctor*

Nurse One .... *Emergency Hospital Tent Nurse*

Forestry Department Chair............... *Professor and Dissertation Committee Member*

Dean .... *University Dean and Dissertation Committee Member*

Cameahwait .... *Keezheekoni's Father and Minister*

Congregation .... *Church Congregation*

Congregation Person One and Two............................ *Member's of Church*

The world's first national park and sanctuary of nature, Yellowstone came under violent attack in the fall of 1988. After a century of fire suppression the forests were overgrown. In 1972 the Let It Burn policy allowed for naturally caused fires to burn out on their own if they did not threaten people or property. Then a Pine Mountain beetle invasion killed thousands of trees, and an eight-year drought dried that dead wood into a tinderbox of epic size. Dry summer storms produced an abundance of lightning that started eighteen major fires that were fueled by raging winds. Half the park was set ablaze. Thousands of firefighters and millions of dollars could not stop the park from burning to ashes. Fine for the adapted lodgepole pine trees whose cones are sealed in a waxy resin that only melts at 140 degrees; in fire. When they released their seeds, the forest was reborn. This was also the time when global warming concerns were born as increasing rates of anthropogenic actions endangered more than just the park. In the end two individuals ended their personal plights in feats of courage against the holy smoke and hellfire.

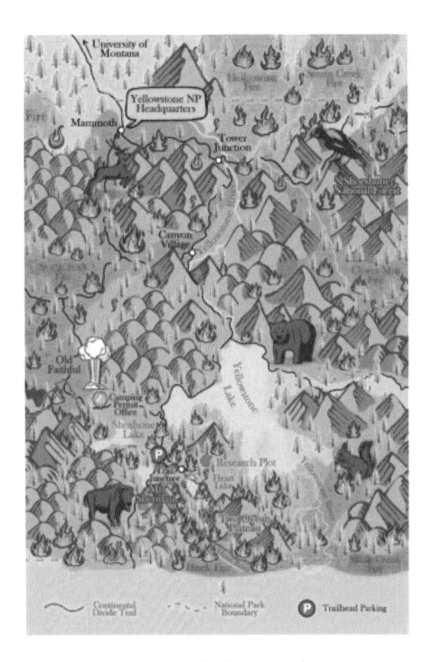

Fig. 1: Map of Yellowstone Fires

FADE IN:

EXT. YELLOWSTONE PARK - LOOKOUT TOWER - DAY

A lookout station stands on a hill where the morning sun glistens over the treetops. From its towering pulpit. FIRE LOOKOUT ONE, female, surveys the large expanse of forest.

In the distance, an ominous cloud explodes with a flash of lightning. The jagged bolt connects the earth and sky. Seconds later, Thor's hammer RESOUNDS.

Fire Lookout One picks up her binoculars. She zeroes in on a small circle of smoking pine trees. The bolt's scorching heat has lit the trunks of several trees like birthday candles planted in the earth.

The fire spreads.

She picks up her radio and holds it in her hands as she continues to observe the fire through her binoculars.

EXT. YELLOWSTONE PARK - SKY RIM LOOP DRIVE - DAY

A dark, menacing thunderhead rises into the troposphere. This king of clouds looms over a quiet street in the woods where double-wide trailers line the road, each with a small patio outside and a mailbox at the end of the driveway.

INT. RANGER'S HOUSING - VICKY'S HOUSE - DAY

VICKY IGLESIAS, late 20s, Latina, hones in on an iMac computer. Notebooks, textbooks, and a coffee mug are strewn around her work desk. She chews her reddened fingernails. Her cuticles are chewed back and scabbed.

SCRUFFY, a good old American mutt, plops her head down at Vicky's feet.

The phone rings.

                    BULLOCK (V.O.)
          Get the final samples yet?

                    VICKY
          We might have enough data. I ran
          an analysis and…

                    BULLOCK (V.O.)
          I want a larger set of data. Size
          matters.

Vicky breathes, calming herself.

                    VICKY
          I need some help with the analy-
          sis.

                    BULLOCK (V.O.)
          You run a regression. I've ex-
          plained it once already, so fig-
          ure it out.

Vicky fidgets with the cord.

                    VICKY
          I will.

                    BULLOCK (V.O.)
          Get those soil tests done, now.

                    VICKY
          I'll go tomorrow.

                    BULLOCK (V.O.)
          You're out of time. Go today.

                    VICKY
          I'm about to head in for the af-
          ternoon shift. I'll go tonight,
          right after that.

                    BULLOCK (V.O.)
          This better be over the moon.
          You're not getting a second
          chance.

Click. Dial tone. She chugs her coffee then gets ready to leave, grabbing her backpack and filling it with notebooks, clothes, food, and equipment.

EXT. YELLOWSTONE NATIONAL PARK - MAMMOTH HOT SPRINGS - DAY

In the northeast corner of the park sits Mammoth Hot Springs with a visitor's center, an old Fort and various businesses that cater to the ubiquitous tourists. The park headquarters is adjoined by a parking lot and large grass field.

INT. SUPERINTENDENT DUKA'S OFFICE - DAY

JOHN DUKA, 60s, clean shaven, paunch, sits at his desk a little tense. He stretches his head left, right, then shrugs his shoulders up, back and down. He sighs.

CODY, Deputy Ranger, 50s, sits across from Duka with LILY, African-American, 40s, glasses, notebook at the ready.

The radio POPS and SCRATCHES.

                    FIRE LOOKOUT ONE (V.O.)
          Sheridan Lookout. Lightning
          strikes west of Mount Sheridan.
          One fire.

                    DUKA
             (over radio)
          Monitor that lighting strike.
          It's a natural fire, we'll follow
          the Let Burn Policy.

                    FIRE LOOKOUT TWO (V.O.)
          Red Fire Tower. Several spot
          fires, small ones, but contained.

                    FIRE LOOKOUT THREE (V.O.)
          Fire at Lake Shoshone. A hundred
          acres near the shoreline. Could
          be man-made.

Duka raises his eyebrows and looks at Lily.

>   LILY
>   The mountain beetle infestation
>   killed thousands of those trees.
>   There's a lot of kindling out
>   there.

>   DUKA
>   (over radio)
>   With a fire that big, all this
>   heat and dry wood, I'll send
>   someone out.

>   FIRE LOOKOUT THREE (V.O.)
>   10-4. Will keep an eye on it.

>   DUKA
>   (over radio)
>   Lookout one and two, if it's not
>   man-made, I can't send in fire
>   suppression, so keep watching
>   them.

Duka puts the mic down and looks at the others.

>   LILY
>   We're in a drought. We need rain.

>   DUKA
>   This is a good way to get rid of
>   Miss Holier Than Thou.

Duka hands Cody the mic.

>   CODY
>   Keezheekoni, do you read? The Su-
>   per wants you.

INT./EXT. SAL'S TRANS AM - OLD FAITHFUL PARKING LOT - DAY

SAL, 25, big forehead, small chin and mouth, wrinkled
business attire, parks a Smokey and the Bandit style
Trans Am. He wears a black fedora. CORNELIUS, 19, a
pumpkin head, a plump body with short and thick
extremities, gets out.

Cornelius reaches in the backseat where Sal's Playboy,
clothes, and small pack are on the seat. He grabs his

over-stuffed backpack, grunting as he lifts it out of the car. He puts it down and takes an orange from the side pocket.

Sal gets out, locks the vehicle, then spritzes a musky cologne on his neck. They head past cars, pickups and RVs with license plates from Florida to Alaska.

At the Old Faithful geyser basin, VISITORS stroll around the boardwalk amid numerous hot springs, mud pots and geysers.

RANGER PATRICK, 30s, bearded and confident, speaks to an eager crowd seated in a semi-circle at Old Faithful geyser.

The world famous geyser steams and sputters.

> PATRICK
> Welcome to the world-famous Old
> Faithful geyser. Magma below the
> surface heats up rainwater. It
> rises as steam but gets blocked,
> then pressure builds until it
> blasts through cracks and up to
> the surface.

As the bubbling and boiling intensify, Vicky and Scruffy walk by.

> PATRICK (CONT'D)
> Hey, Vicky! Hit the switch.

> VICKY
> Okay, I'm on my way.

Sal's eyes lock onto Vicky's svelte figure as she crosses behind the crowd.

> PATRICK
> I'm kidding, everybody. Enjoy the
> show!

Vicky saunters by the grass field in front of the park office. Sal stares at her, feasting his eyes on each swing of her hips.

                         SAL
                   (to Cornelius)
               Hello Dolly!

Vicky disappears into the park office with a sign posted
outside that says "Camping and Backwoods Permits".

At Old Faithful, people ready cameras and camcorders.
Old Faithful erupts with a blasting gush of steam and
water. The crowd jumps up in excitement. The explosion
intensifies, and they draw back in awe.

                         SAL (CONT'D)
                   (motioning to Old Faithful)
               So virulent.

In less than a minute, Old faithful dies down.

                         CORNELIUS
               Thanks for the ride, Sal. I got
               to go to the permit office over
               there.

Sal's eyes sparkle.

                         SAL
               I think I'll go, too.

Cornelius looks confused.

                         CORNELIUS
               You ever been camping?

Sal slicks back his hair.

                         SAL
               I slept on a few couches before.
               Besides, that fine girl with the
               you-know-what went in there.

INT. PARK PERMIT OFFICE - DAY

Long fluorescent bulbs illuminate the office. A few
black and white nature shots sheathed in plastic
frames hang on the wood-paneled walls. Vicky leans on
the long counter studying a log sheet.

Sal sidles up as close as he can to Vicky. He tilts his hat, striking the pose of a model in an outdoor clothing catalog.

Scruffy walks to the visitor side of the counter, circles and then plops down.

>   SAL
>   So this is where the switch is
>   that turns on Old Faithful, wink
>   wink.

Vicky returns a blank look, and Scruffy emits a soft growl.

Cornelius reaches out his hand and pets Scruffy who in turn wags her tail.

>   CORNELIUS
>   I love dogs.

>   VICKY
>   She's a better friend than...

>   CORNELIUS
>   ...some people.

Vicky smiles at Cornelius and their eyes connect.

>   VICKY
>   Can I help you?

>   SAL
>   I want to go frolicking in na-
>   ture's playground, amid the tran-
>   quil spirit of a midsummer night,
>   under a star-lit sky.

>   CORNELIUS
>   I need a camping site.

She consults the permit log as Patrick walks in.

>   VICKY
>   We don't have any available for
>   tonight.

Vicky closes the book.

                    PATRICK
          And there aren't any hotel rooms
          within three hundred miles.

                    SAL
          Great.

                    CORNELIUS
          What can we do?

                    PATRICK
          Drive 'til you find a place. Mis-
          soula, maybe Boise?

                    VICKY
          And all backwoods camping sites
          are closed for now. Only hiking's
          allowed.

                    CORNELIUS
          Is there a good hike to do?

Vicky takes out a map and puts it on the counter.

                    VICKY
          Heart Lake's pretty. It's a five
          mile hike. You could easily do it
          tomorrow.

                    PATRICK
          We recommend a party of four out
          there. It's grizzly country.

                    SAL
          How's two?

                    PATRICK
          Better than one, not as good as
          three.

                    VICKY
          Come back in the morning. Maybe a
          campsite will open up.

                    SAL
          This is a bit frustrating. We
          should talk it over.

Sal pulls Cornelius aside.

                    CORNELIUS
          I don't have a car. I don't have
          a place to camp. I'll go out
          there and pitch a tent.

                    SAL
          I want to pitch a tent, too. I'd
          like to get my prairie dog down
          that gopher hole if you know what
          I mean.

                    CORNELIUS
          What? You think she likes you?

                    SAL
          She's a naturalist. They like
          green, and I got plenty.

Sal looks over at Vicky, eavesdropping on her conversation.

                    PATRICK
          Maria saw your light on at two in
          the morning.

                    VICKY
          Finishing the dissertation.

                    PATRICK
          Isn't a lack of sleep counterpro-
          ductive? Stress impairs thinking,
          memory, and decision making.

Vicky holds a mug filled with coffee.

                    VICKY
          Three cups this morning. I'm
          good.

PATRICK
Just think, once you get your
PhD, you can unlock the advisor's
ball and chain.

Vicky waves a stamped envelope.

VICKY
I'll still be a slave. Graduate
school loans don't pay for themselves.

PATRICK
Is the research finished?

VICKY
I have to hike to Heart Lake
tonight. Dr. Bullock wants one
more set of data.

Sal's eyes brighten. He eavesdrops more intensely.

PATRICK
It is so much work for those
PhD's. You must have covered
every acre in the southeast park
by now.

VICKY
This is the last one. When our
shift is over, I'll hustle out
there, camp, then get it done by
early tomorrow.

PATRICK
I'll be demolishing our office to
make way for a crib room.

VICKY
Did Maria like the baby names I
suggested?

PATRICK
You want something Spanish,
Keezheekoni wants her to be named
after something in nature, so
we'll have to see.

Sal makes up his mind.

SAL
I'll hike, too. Been driving for
days and I hate sleeping in the
car.

CORNELIUS
Do you have any camping gear?

SAL
These are desperate times.

CORNELIUS
Ever been in a forest?

SAL
Yeah, Central Park.

CORNELIUS
You're in a button-down shirt?

SAL
Business casual; and every girl's
crazy about a sharp-dressed man.

Sal spins Cornelius back to the counter with his arm
over his shoulder, all buddy-buddy.

SAL (CONT'D)
We'll come back tomorrow. And
hike to Heart Lake.

CORNELIUS
Do you know what the weather's
gonna' be?

PATRICK
Some lightning, no rain.

                    SAL
          Electricity's in the air.

                    VICKY
          It starts fires.

                    SAL
          Romantic?

                    VICKY
          Dangerous; and don't wear any
          cologne out there either.

                    PATRICK
          Cook meat in a T-shirt, wash it
          five times and a bear will still
          smell the shirt from five miles
          away.

                    CORNELIUS
          Is that true?

                    PATRICK
          Maybe.

Vicky looks at Cornelius then Sal, measuring them up.
She unfolds the map on the countertop, puts a big star
next to the trailhead and draws a line to Heart Lake.

                    VICKY
          Park at the trailhead, follow
          this path to the Mount Sheridan
          Trail juncture, then head left to
          Heart Lake.

Vicky draws a red circle and labels it "BEAR HABITAT".
Sal notices her fingernails are ripped up and red.

                    VICKY (CONT'D)
          Stay out of here. It's bear coun-
          try.

                    SAL
          The land of beauty and the
          beasts.

                    VICKY
          Should I put you on the waitlist
          for a campsite?

                    CORNELIUS
          Sure.

                    SAL
          It's Sal.

                    VICKY
          I need one of you to sign.

She holds out a pen. Sal and Cornelius both go for it,
so she puts it back.

                    SAL
          I'll rock, paper, scissors you
          for it?

Sal and Cornelius each holds out a fist.

                    SAL AND CORNELIUS
               (pump fists up and down four times)
          Once, twice, three, shoot.

Cornelius plays paper to Sal's rock and wins.

                    VICKY
               (holding the pen)
          What's your name?

                    CORNELIUS
          Cornelius Hedges.

Vicky's eyes lock onto Cornelius then to Patrick as
raises her eyebrows.

                    CORNELIUS (CONT'D)
          I'm on a pilgrimage to where my
          great- great-grandfather ex-
          plored.

> VICKY
> He helped preserve this park for
> future generations. He did it for
> you then, right?

> SAL
> I'm on an existential journey to
> reflect amid nature's cornucopia.

Sal takes out a pen with "Leibowitz and Constantini Law
$5,000,000" stamped on it. He flourishes it around to
flash her the dollar amount.

> SAL
> Use this pen.

Vicky ignores Sal, still intrigued by Cornelius who
signs his name. Vicky hands them the map. Sal reaches
out for it, trying to brush her hand. Vicky veers toward
Cornelius, giving it to him.

> VICKY
> Enjoy the hike.

Sal glances at her nametag then tips his hat.

> SAL
> Hope to see y'all down the trail.

They leave.

> PATRICK
> Hear that guy? He was flirting
> badly.

> VICKY
> Doesn't matter. I have no time
> for a social life.

EXT. PARK PERMIT OFFICE - DAY

Outside the office, Cornelius studies the map.

Sal removes a piece of paper from his pocket. At the
top, he writes "Sal A. Schussman vs Vicky Iglesias" then

he writes "bites nails" and "preoccupied with something and/or someone." He puts the paper and pen back in his pocket.

> SAL
> Let me have that.

Sal takes the map from Cornelius and looks at the hike. He rubs the stubble on his chin.

> SAL (CONT'D)
> I think I'll grow a beard. *Luck Be a Lady Tonight.*

INT. SUPERINTENDENT DUKA'S OFFICE - DAY

KEEZHEEKONI, 30s, a Native American female walks by a brass plaque inscribed with "Superintendent Duka" and into the office where she stands in front of his desk. She's tall, has long black hair and wears a white beaded tribal choker.

> DUKA
> Just who I was looking for. I fi-
> nally have that opportunity you
> wanted so badly.

> KEEZHEEKONI
> That's why I left the rez and
> came here to my people's land.

> DUKA
> It's the US government's land
> now.

Duka looks over some files and papers.

> DUKA (CONT'D)
> (sarcastically)
> Let's see what I got for you. A
> toilet exploded at Grant Village.
> Yuck. A teen messing with a bison
> got a horn jammed up his tush.
> Ouch. Shame there's only one of
> you.

Duka hands her the papers.

> DUKA (CONT'D)
> There's a suspicious fire at
> Shoshone Lake.

> KEEZHEEKONI
> Probably someone being careless.

> DUKA
> We're in a drought and there's a
> lot of wood out there. Check it
> out. And take that choker off.
> You're a ranger, not Sacajawea.

> KEEZHEEKONI
> That's Sa-ka-ga-we-a.

> DUKA
> Just get out of here already.

Keezheekoni complies with dignity and leaves. Duka tugs
on his short white hair.

INT./EXT. SAL'S TRANS AM - DAY - (MOVING)

Sal is about to pull into the parking area for the Mount
Sheridan and Heart Lake Trails when he spots an access
road just ahead. He pulls past the parking lot and onto
the grassy road driving down a short way then veers into
the woods.

> SAL
> No one will know we're sneaking
> out here illegally or break into
> this beauty.

He pulls in through the trees and brush with the skill
of a driver who navigated busy New York City traffic his
whole life. In twenty seconds, he hides the car from
street view.

> CORNELIUS
> There's no one even out here.

They get out. Sal strokes the curve of the hood.

>   SAL
>   I take no chances with her. Just
>   look at that body and trim.

Sal changes into khaki shorts and puts his belt back on.
He rolls up his sleeves, takes the pack from the back
seat and goes to the trunk for a quilt, shirt, and
sweater.

Cornelius grunts as he slings on his overloaded backpack. Once set, he gnaws at the beef jerky in his hand.

EXT. TRAILHEAD - DAY

At the trailhead marker, a large board has a display
with instructions to hang food, boil water and camp only
in designated areas. On a large map, Cornelius follows
the trail with his finger past the Mt. Sheridan Trail
juncture to Heart Lake.

>   CORNELIUS
>   There's a site, there, at Heart
>   Lake.

>   SAL
>   There's only one way in and out,
>   thus I hope to run into that
>   ranger.

>   CORNELIUS
>   Can we make it? It's a long hike.

Sal looks at the large belly of Cornelius.

>   SAL
>   Speak for yourself. I hike the
>   crowded concrete city sidewalks
>   every day.

They stride off by a giant wooden cutout of Smokey the
Bear and disappear under the canopy of lodgepole pine
trees.

EXT. OLD FAITHFUL GEYSER - DAY

Vicky talks to a small group of tourists. A WOMAN and small CHILD, 7, are in front.

                CHILD
        Why do I see lightning, but then
        no rain comes?

                VICKY
        They're dry thunderstorms.

                CHILD
        Why?

                VICKY
        The air is so dry that when the
        raindrops fall, they evaporate.

                CHILD
        Doesn't that just make more rain
        clouds?

Vicky smiles then looks at her watch. It's 8 P.M.

EXT. YELLOWSTONE FOREST - DAY

Blackened earth and burned trees smolder as fire spreads through the brush and pine needles. The wind picks up and instantly the fires rise into the treetops.

EXT. MOUNT SHERIDAN/HEART LAKE TRAIL FORK - DAY

Worn out, Sal and Cornelius stop at the sign marking the juncture of the Mt. Sheridan and Heart Lake trails. Sweat soaks Cornelius. His hair and face dripping with it. One arrow on the sign points to the right for Mt. Sheridan and one arrow points to the left for Heart Lake. They head left.

EXT. HEART LAKE/ MT. SHERIDAN TRAILHEAD - TWILIGHT

In civilian clothes, Vicky parks in the trailhead lot. She and Scruffy get out. She puts a trowel in the bag and checks for her pencil and notebook. She doesn't notice that her walkie-talkie falls between the seats.

The winds are blustery and carry a few clouds of thick smoke.

> VICKY
> Caramba! What is all this smoke?

With only a little daylight remaining, she adjusts her headlamp.

> VICKY (CONT'D)
> It's getting dark. We have to
> hurry. ¿Listo?

She dons her backpack then she and Scruffy head out and disappear into the darkening woods.

EXT. HEART LAKE - DAY

Sal and Cornelius find an empty campsite on the shores of Heart Lake. In a clearing of pine trees, there's a picnic table, a fire pit full of black ash, and a twelve foot bear pole.

A bolt of lightning connects the earth and sky.

> SAL
> Whoa!

Thunder reverberates. Cornelius grabs his stomach.

> CORNELIUS
> That was my stomach. I'm hungry.

> SAL
> Keep it down. Trying to do a lit-
> tle thinking out here.

Cornelius sets up a pole frame and nylon tent. When he forces a stake into the stiff dry ground, the metal bends.

PIONEER, 44, anemic, with a long scraggly beard and a

red bandana around his neck, emerges from behind a tree. He wears a bright friendly smile and holds a "Logger" beer.

Pioneer reaches his hand out to Cornelius.

>   PIONEER (CONT'D)
>   Howdy. Folks call me Pioneer.

Cornelius is confused. He looks around trying to see where Pioneer came from.

>   CORNELIUS
>   Ahhh, Cornelius. Hi.

Sal looks at Pioneer, then around the campground and back at Pioneer. Sal firmly shakes his hand for a few seconds, looking him in the eye and sizing him up.

>   SAL
>   Good to meet you, I'm Sal.

Pioneer swigs the beer. Sal smells the alcohol and life stress emanating from this scraggly backwoodsman.

>   SAL
>   How is it that you're camping out
>   here? We were told it's closed.

>   PIONEER
>   I'm homesteading. Excepting the
>   nation's no longer honoring
>   squatter's rights.

>   SAL
>   My legal advice is don't give up.
>   Constant appeals can wear a judge
>   out.

>   CORNELIUS
>   I'm gonna eat. Been thinking
>   about food ever since we started
>   hiking.

Cornelius deliberately lays out a smorgasbord, standing up one item at a time in front of him; a bag of bagels,

a box of Skittles, a wrapped meat stick, and a cookie
tin. He takes a handful of cookies out. Sal and Pioneer
eye him.

> CORNELIUS (CONT'D)
> What? I love cookies.

Cornelius slobbers the cookie down, barely chewing it
before he gulps. Sal and Pioneer watch him agape and
aghast as Cornelius now stuffs a bagel in his pie hole
then starts chomping everything else.

> SAL
> (imitating Marlin Perkins)
> The grizzly bear always prepares
> for the worst of winters! You'll
> be prepared for an emergency too
> with insurance from Mutual of Om-
> aha's Wild Kingdom!

Cornelius laughs then chokes.

> CORNELIUS
> I can't help it. Once I start, I
> can't stop.

Pioneer holds up an empty beer bottle.

> PIONEER
> I know the feeling.

Cornelius now opens the candy box and pours the Skittles
in his mouth. There is a GNASHING of teeth.

> SAL
> You gotta a hollow leg? One with
> a hole on the bottom?

> PIONEER
> I have that same problem. When I
> drink, I spring a leak.

> SAL
> Where are the vegetables?

                    CORNELIUS
I'm allergic to them.

                    SAL
Which ones?

                    CORNELIUS
All of them.

                    SAL
Your reaction to food isn't at
all normal.

                    CORNELIUS
I kind of hate myself for being
like this.

                    SAL
It can't be that bad.

                    CORNELIUS
I'm a loner so I eat when I get
bored.

Pioneer points to the table that is already littered
with crumbs and pieces of food.

                    PIONEER
This might be one reason for you
being so isolated and alone.

                    SAL
Pioneer, how'd you get that name?

                    PIONEER
I dig in dumpsters for aluminum
cans. One plug nickel each.

                    SAL
       (using air quotes)
A "pioneer" and a "prospector".

                    PIONEER
          And I'm in big trouble with the
          missus.

                    SAL
          The drinking?

                    PIONEER
          I tried to stop, but one beer
          leads to another... five or six.

                    SAL
          I got woman troubles too. Got put
          on leave from the firm. Something
          in me said go see Yogi the Bear.
          I love me some cartoons.

Cornelius looks at Pioneer and points his thumb at Sal.

                    CORNELIUS
          I'm glad you came out here.
          He picked me up hitchhiking.

                    PIONEER
          We three have a lot in common.

                    SAL
          We're homeless, rejected by
          women, and don't have jobs?

Pioneer and Sal look at Cornelius.

                    CORNELIUS
          Yup. I got fired from a pizza
          shop. Got caught eating a pizza
          crust in the mop closet, cheddar
          cheese in the freezer, then the
          owner saw me taking a bite from a
          customer's salad.

                    SAL
          Hard to deny you figuratively ate
          into his money when you literally
          ate the dough, the cheddar, and
          the lettuce.

> CORNELIUS
> I didn't think of it 'til now,
> but I also ate the cabbage.

> PIONEER
> Huzzah!

> CORNELIUS
> I'll eat anything. Except Lima
> beans. That's where I draw the
> line.

The tall thin pines around the campsite surround them,
lining up like prison bars.

INT. SUPERINTENDENT DUKA'S OFFICE - NIGHT

Keezheekoni enters Duka's office with a bag of evidence.

> DUKA
> You're back? What about the fire
> at Shoshone Lake?

> KEEZHEEKONI
> No mystery.

She hands him a bag. Duka sees it contains a few "Logger" beer bottles and a small burnt section of an old
newspaper crossword puzzle.

> KEEZHEEKONI (CONT'D)
> It was man-made, but it's going
> out on its own.

> DUKA
> Thank God you said that. I mean,
> it's fire season, but if you say
> so, must be true.

> KEEZHEEKONI
> Dependent on winds and...

Duka points to his white hair.

                    DUKA
                (interrupting)
          Do you know why I'm getting snow
          on top of this roof?

                    KEEZHEEKONI
          On the medicine wheel, white is
          clouds and moon, North in
          winter...

                    DUKA
                (interrupting again)
          This park contains thousands and
          thousands of acres of forest.
          We're in an eight-year drought
          and there's lightning storms
          every day.

                    KEEZHEEKONI
          This is the way of Mother Earth.

                    DUKA
          I'm the steward of this land and
          I have a million visitors to care
          for, so go.

EXT. RESEARCH PLOT IN FOREST - NIGHT

Vicky sits up in her tent. Scruffy sprawls out beside
her. Vicky takes a sip from the water bottle and shines
the headlamp on a clipboard. The paper contains many
filled-out columns and rows. The bottom ones are empty.

                    VICKY
          Será un gran día mañana. Que
          duermas bien, perrito.

She pets Scruffy, then turns off the light, settling
into her sleeping bag.

EXT. HEART LAKE CAMPSITE - NIGHT

Sal and Cornelius sit on logs around the fire. A tipsy
Pioneer takes center stage.

                    PIONEER
          I got a history award in high
          school. Did impersonations; Peter
          Newton, Nero, Lincoln...

Sal waves his hat, putting an abrupt stop to Pioneer.

                    SAL
          Don't sacrilege the name of Lin-
          coln. I wear this hat in his hon-
          or.

                    CORNELIUS
          It's a cool fedora.

Sal shows Cornelius the label.

                    SAL
          A Stetson. Got it at my bar mitz-
          vah. First time I wore it.

                    PIONEER
          Five bucks if you can tell me
          what Lincoln kept in his hat.

                    SAL
          His brains?

                    PIONEER
          Letters, speeches, documents,
          probably the grocery list from
          his wife.

                    SAL
          I should do that, too, in homage
          to that great man.

Sal takes the paper from his pocket and stuffs it into
the crown of the hat.

                    CORNELIUS
          Can you do an imitation of some-
          one from the history of Yellow-
          stone?

                    PIONEER
Jim Bridger, the hunter and fur
trapper. There's a good chance
your grandfather met him.

                    CORNELIUS
Did he know Cornelius Hedges?

                    PIONEER
Wait, is your name Cornelius
Hedges?

                    CORNELIUS
Yup. My great great grandfather
came here on an expedition.

                    PIONEER
Jim Bridger probably knew him.

Pioneer picks up a long stick and aims it like a rifle,
squinting through the "sight". He snaps the gun on his
shoulder then shifts to the two-handed ready carry posi-
tion.

                    PIONEER (CONT'D)
Was out in the backwoods one
night. Real tired. I came to the
Grand Canyon of the Yellowstone
and before bedtime, I yelled,
"Hey, you!" Come morning, the
echo woke me up.

                    CORNELIUS
          (chuckling)
Nature's alarm clock.

                    PIONEER
That morning I snuck into these
here private lands and caught me
some bass. Boiled 'em right in a
hot spring. It was illegal, mind
you, but I like my fish poached.

                    SAL
          (playing air drums)
Ba da bing!

>   PIONEER
> Breakfast smelled great. All of a
> sudden a grizzly came into camp.
> Chased me clear up a tree. I
> threw my boots at it and it was
> so mean it just picked 'em up and
> threw 'em right back at me!

Pioneer bows and almost falls. Sal and Cornelius clap.

>   PIONEER (CONT'D)
> My kids love that story.

Off balance, Pioneer gazes skyward. It's an almost dead
moon except for a sliver of white that looks a sickle in
the sky.

>   PIONEER (CONT'D)
> No more beer baby. I want you
> back.

Pioneer holds his heart. He gets a tear.

>   PIONEER (CONT'D)
> You're m' best friend, Debra.
> Take off, De-bra... baby.

Pioneer cackles, then puts his hands in the air as if
holding onto motorcycle handlebars.

>   PIONEER (CONT'D)
> Vrum, vrum, vrooooom.

Pioneer drives off the phantasmal motorcycle, zig-zag-
ging into the woods, leaving the men at the smoldering
campfire. Sal looks at the tent. The sides droop.

>   SAL
> Should I get a cab to take us
> back to the hotel?

The tent falls flat.

>   CORNELIUS
> What do you want? It's designed
> for easy take down.

          SAL
Where'd you get it? Charlie
Brown's Camping Store?

EXT. YELLOWSTONE PARK - NIGHT

All over the park, heavy winds blow hard and expand into
infernos. One after another, these dangerous, out of
control fires, charge through the forest, leaping their
way through and over the trees.

EXT. YELLOWSTONE PARK - DAY

Several miles west of Heart Lake, gale-forced winds blow
the dry tinder into blazes that climb the trees. A chain
reaction of fires goes off, lighting a thousand blazes.
The fires storm toward Heart Lake like a marching army.

INT. SUPERINTENDENT DUKA'S OFFICE - DAY

In Superintendent Duka's office, he and Cody are busy
arranging schedules and reports and listening to the
radio.

          FIRE LOOKOUT ONE (V.O.)
   Fire-Lookout One.

          DUKA
   Go ahead, Lookout One.

          FIRE LOOKOUT ONE (V.O.)
     (alarmed)
   Fires west of Mt. Sheridan
   headin' east. Wind's 'r pickin'
   up.

          DUKA
   Ah, Jesus! Hold on.

Duka covers the mic with his hand.

>   DUKA (CONT'D)
>   (to Cody)
>   Did you check all the backcountry
>   permits?
>
>   CODY
>   (to Duka)
>   Backwoods were closed two days
>   ago.
>
>   DUKA
>   (to Cody)
>   Good. We don't want any idiots
>   out there.
>
>   FIRE LOOKOUT TWO (V.O.)
>   Fire in northeast park. Already a
>   thousand acres.
>
>   DUKA
>   I'll send some men in.
>
>   FIRE LOOKOUT TWO (O.S.)
>   They're remote. They about to hit
>   Montana. Heading right toward the
>   National Forest.
>
>   DUKA
>   10-4. I will call in a team of
>   smokejumpers.
>
>   FIRE LOOKOUT THREE (V.O.)
>   Shoshone fire's huge. It's on its
>   way to Roosevelt Parkway.

EXT. HEART LAKE/ MT. SHERIDAN TRAILHEAD PARKING LOT - SAME

Heavy winds blow fires over the Roosevelt Parkway into the Heart Lake Trailhead parking lot. Vicky's car is quick to ignite and Sal's Trans Am EXPLODES. Car pieces fly in the air, leaving a smoking frame with burning tires.

At the Heart Lake Trail entrance, Smokey the Bear cannot prevent itself from going up in flames. Fire gallops down the trail into the woods.

EXT. RANGER'S HOUSING - DAY

MARIA, 30s, in the full bloom of pregnancy, opens the
screen door in her bathrobe and sits on a front patio
deck chair.

Patrick comes out with two cups of coffee. Small chinks
of burning debris fall from the sky and smoke blows
every which way.

                    PATRICK
          Ash is falling. Maybe we should
          go inside.

                    MARIA
          I hope this ends soon. Our baby's
          gonna need fresh air.

Maria caresses her soccer ball-sized stomach.

                    PATRICK
          The super just called all the
          smokejumpers in for fire service.

Maria grabs Patrick's arm.

                    MARIA
          Are you crazy?

                    PATRICK
          It's overtime pay. I thought you
          wanted those environmentally
          friendly cloth diapers.

                    MARIA
          You have a baby on the way.

                    PATRICK
          The park needs me. I'm a highly
          skilled smokejumper.

Maria tilts her head forward. Her face tightens. She
places his hand on her tummy and glares at him.

               MARIA
          The baby needs a father.

Patrick rubs her tummy. The baby kicks.

               PATRICK
          Feel that? He's kicking me outta
          here.

               MARIA
          She's not happy daddy isn't lis-
          tening. You were gonna' demolish
          the office for the crib room, re-
          member?

               PATRICK
          You knew about this when we mar-
          ried. I'll always be there for my
          brothers.

               MARIA
          The child and this family are
          your priority now.

               PATRICK
          I'm protecting you, the child,
          everyone. We all need to be safe.

Maria gets up. Patrick grabs her hand trying to be ro-
mantic.

               PATRICK (CONT'D)
          I have ten minutes before work.
          Can I get a down payment on the
          carpentry work?

Patrick winks. Maria turns away and goes inside. Patrick
gets up, then sits down. He gets up again and goes to
his truck.

EXT. WEST OF MT. SHERIDAN - DAY

Fires climb the Red Mountains in a long line of flames.
Ferocious winds send blasts of embers eastward. The
burning mayhem crests Mount Sheridan, which overlooks

the now peaceful Heart Lake and start heading down
the forest on the other side.

EXT. RESEARCH PLOT IN FOREST - DAY

In an opening of forest already burnt by fire, Vicky
kneels within a circle of string that is thirty feet in
radius. As she counts pinecones and seeds, smoke swirls
by. She examines a roasted and open pinecone as fires
roar in the distance.

Vicky and Scruffy are inundated by thick clouds of
smoke.

                    VICKY
          Jesucristo!

She winds up the string then squints through the thick
haze at Scruffy, worried. She places the stakes, dirt
specimens, and a clipboard in her backpack.

A frightened Scruffy whines.

                    VICKY (CONT'D)
          Nos vámonos.

They take off.

EXT. MOUNT SHERIDAN/HEART LAKE TRAIL - DAY

Gusty breezes blow smoke all around Sal, Pioneer, and
Cornelius. Pioneer marches forward, coughing. He holds
pace with Sal, whose brisk stride is that of a big city
lawyer. Cornelius shuffles behind, gasping for breath.

                    PIONEER
          Nothing like sleeping in the
          trustworthy hands of Mother Na-
          ture.

                    SAL
          Not me. Cornelius farted so much.
          The tent smelled like rotten eggs
          the whole night.

> PIONEER
> I woke up in a trench. Must've
> dug it in my sleep.

> SAL
> Of course I've heard of people
> doing weird things in their
> sleep, but never sleep digging?

> PIONEER
> It's the PTSD.

They stop at the Mount Sheridan and Heart Lake trail
juncture. Sal studies the map. Smoke and burning ash
drift by ominously. Small embers land and smolder in the
ground cover and the sparks turn into flames.

> PIONEER (CONT'D)
> (to Cornelius)
> Hurry up! We need to get out of
> Dodge.

Sal watches Cornelius who grunts along as he catches up.

> SAL
> How much can one person sweat?

Over the mountains, a plume of smoke rises a mile high.

In front of it, a fire wall with fifty foot flaming
spikes sends a thick pall of smoke filled with soot and
ash floating by Sal and Pioneer.

Cornelius arrives. An ember drops. Burning missiles
WHISTLE through the air.

> PIONEER
> (yelling)
> Incoming!

The firebrands EXPLODE and instantly erupt into flames.

A red-orange juggernaut of flaming trees barrels down
the mountain with a tumultuous hue and cry.

The sky rains red, orange and yellow. The ground ignites, burns up the trees, and the tops burst into

blazes.

> PIONEER (CONT'D)
>> (yelling louder)
> Firestorm!

A hand-sized ember smacks Sal's face.

> SAL
> ARRRGHH!

Sal drops the map and wipes the burning ash from his cheek. The map flits along the ground, hits a large rock, and stops.

Three deer bound through the trees and flames, over the trail, by the men, and back into the woods.

> PIONEER
> Let's go!

Fires block the hiking trail in front, to the right and behind them. Pioneer shoves Sal into the woods. They follow the same escape path the deer used, heading into the woods and Cornelius follows.

The men scramble forward, scampering over branches and logs through the uncut, off-trail terrain. Each person moves at his top speed as the inferno razes through the brush and trees.

The smoke churns so violently that Cornelius can barely distinguish Sal and Pioneer through the burning ahead of him. His feet pound the forest floor, and his heart booms.

Above Sal and Pioneer, the top of a burning tree falls from a two-hundred-foot-high conifer. It hits the ground and explodes. Its branches smack the ground on impact, right next to Pioneer, and knock him over. He gets up, smacks off the flames and runs.

Through pine trees and downed wood, Pioneer and Sal ascend a small hill in front of Cornelius.

EXT. FOREST HILL - CONTINUOUS

Pioneer and Sal stop and look back. Cornelius staggers through burning debris and tree limbs at the bottom of the hill. Embers drop around him. Pioneer places a bandanna over his nose and mouth and peers through the trees.

                    PIONEER
          Double time, soldier!

                    CORNELIUS
          Wait!

Cornelius slips, then gets up. His pack snags a branch. Cornelius yanks and tugs at it desperately.

Fire reflects in Pioneer's glazed-over eyes as he focuses his line of sight down the hill.

                    PIONEER
          Civilian!

The roar is deafening.

                    SAL
               (yelling)
          What? We gotta get outta here!

                    PIONEER
          No one left behind!

The fire appears from behind a cloud of smoke and closes in on Cornelius. The smoke and flames obscure him. The fires leaps up the hill.

                    SAL
               (shaking Pioneer)
          There's nothing we can do!

Sal pulls a resisting Pioneer and half-drags him down the other side of the hill.

EXT. BOTTOM OF FOREST HILL - CONTINUOUS

Cornelius wrenches himself free. By now the fire is in front of him. He looks up, through the flames, and into the wall of fire. He does not see his friends.

>   CORNELIUS
>   Hey!

Cornelius retreats, withdrawing away from the burning bushes, scrambles back through the churning, roiling smoke. He weaves clumsily back to the left, dodging flaming branches and jumping over burning downfall.

EXT. YELLOWSTONE PARK - LOOKOUT TOWER - DAY

Fire Lookout One scampers down the trail amid igniting trees and impending doom. Behind her, on the hill, smoke and fire appear at the base of the lookout tower.

EXT. PARK HEADQUARTERS - DAY

Firefighting trucks, park vehicles, pick-ups, etc. crowd the parking lot. Two large canvas tents have sprung up in the field. Red cones cordon off an area on one side where MICHAEL, late 20s and clean-cut, inspects a clean and shiny helicopter.

An American Red Cross sign is posted outside the smaller tent. DR. YOUNG, 40s, African-American, and JULIE, nurse, 30s, go in the tent carrying medical equipment and supplies.

PARK SERVICE and LOCAL FIREFIGHTING flow into the larger tent along with numerous EMERGENCY PERSONNEL.

INT. FIRE FIGHTING HQ MEETING TENT - CONTINUOUS

A trove of green, brown and yellow uniformed FIREFIGHT-ERS sit themselves in front of a podium. The group is mostly men.

Cody and Lily stand in front with Duka. Next to them is a table with maps spread out and a few piles of folders.

Duka moves in front of the podium. There is a quiet moment as the firefighters settle down in their seats.

> DUKA
> I closed the park and we are
> evacuating all the non-emergency
> personnel. The Secretary of the
> Interior, Bob Kendall, suspended
> the Let It Burn policy. That
> means we fight every fire in the
> park, even if it's not man-made.
> There are twelve fire fronts that
> are of unprecedented magnitude.
> Let's hear from Lily, the park's
> fire behavior specialist, and
> then you'll get your assignments.

Lily moves to the podium and adjusts her glasses.

> LILY
> The weather calls for no rain and
> high winds, gusts up to eighty
> miles an hour. Relative humidity
> figures are in the single digits,
> so fires start easily. Right now
> they're burning so fast that they
> create their own updrafts that
> fan the flames even further.

She slides over.

> DUKA
> This will take all our manpower
> and equipment.

Duka wheezes. He wipes sweat from his brow and looks over the wide-eyed and tight-mouthed crews.

> DUKA (CONT'D)
> Without rain, fire suppression of
> this type is impossible, so pray
> for it. Your assignments are
> ready. Be safe and Godspeed!

Cody and Lily distribute maps and assignments to the crew chiefs who grab them and go. Duka motions for Keezheekoni and Patrick. They hurry over.

                    DUKA (CONT'D)
              (to Keezheekoni)
        You want a big job, right? You're
        to build a firebreak.

Duka shows Keezheekoni a map on the table.

                    DUKA (CONT'D)
        In front of the Snake River fire
        complex, here.

Keezheekoni nods.

                    DUKA (CONT'D)
        Hike in from the southeast. Put
        it on the eastern side of the
        meadow.

                    KEEZHEEKONI
        Yes, sir.

Keezheekoni leaves with a WAR CRY. Duka cringes.

                    DUKA (CONT'D)
              (to Patrick)
        The Hellroaring fire's here and
        it's closing in on the Shoshone
        National Forest.

                    PATRICK
        That's a lot of valuable timber.

                    DUKA
        There's a Twin Otter at the
        airstrip. Take the smokejumpers.
                    PATRICK
        Will do.

Duka again points to a map.

                    DUKA
        Land behind this small fire here.
        Work through across this slope to
        the northeast. The Gulch fire's
        here.

                    PATRICK
I'll have my parents get Maria.
There's something I have to tell
you.

                    DUKA
Make it fast.

                    PATRICK
Vicky went to check her research
plots.

                    DUKA
For Christ's sake! Where is she?

                    PATRICK
In the section of the forest
northwest of Heart Lake.

                    DUKA
Not a word. Do you hear?

                    PATRICK
Yes, sir.

                    DUKA
I'll look for her myself.

                    PATRICK
Go easy on her. She's under a lot
of pressure.

                    DUKA
I'm the least of her problems.

Patrick leaves as Cody comes over.

                    DUKA (CONT'D)
Evacuate all non-essential personnel. Set up crews to guard
this office, the med tents and
Old Faithful Lodge. I'll be back.

EXT. PARK HEADQUARTERS - DAY

Trucks and buses are lined up in a staging area on the parking lot side of the field where a chaotic crowd of firemen equip the vehicles and prepare to head out.

A local news van prepares to broadcast. ANN MARANEK, stand up person and reporter, 30s, the beauty pageant type who can talk in front of a camera, gets the signal from a CAMERAMAN, 20s.

> ANN MARANEK
> Yellowstone, America's beloved
> park, burns today. Thousands of
> acres of forest are up in smoke
> and flames.

The cameraman pans the area.

> ANN MARANEK (CONT'D)(O.S.)
> Crews ready themselves and head
> out to do heroic battle with what
> seem to be untamable fires.

Firefighters scurry around, loading their transport vehicles. Duka boards a helicopter. It lifts up and flies overhead.

Patrick and a crew of six smokejumpers load into a park service Suburban. The last man jumps and they roll out.

Keezheekoni checks over headlamps, first aid kits, axes, Pulaskis, water and emergency fireproof shelters then mounts a small bus with a twelve-person brigade on board.

INT. BUS - DAY

Keezheekoni faces the crew.

> KEEZHEEKONI
> We're heading in front of the
> Snake River complex, to build a
> firebreak.

FIREFIGHTER ONE, 30s, African-American, straightens up.

> FIREFIGHTER ONE
> Don't those work one in a hundred
> times?

> KEEZHEEKONI
> We can do this. And show respect
> for Mother Nature. She's on the
> warpath.

EXT. YELLOWSTONE PARK ENTRANCE - DAY

The American and Wyoming flags, lifted by a stiff, smoky breeze, blow sideways. Rangers direct a steady stream of cars, buses, RV's and trucks out of the park, passing the Park Service sign that reads, "Welcome to Yellowstone".

On the other side of the highway, the park authorities usher in a large armada of firefighters, firefighting and emergency vehicles, as well as the United States military. The noisy trucks rumble into the park.

EXT. YELLOWSTONE FOREST WEST OF HEART LAKE - SAME

Pioneer and Sal surge forward through a labyrinth of burning trees, underbrush and darkness.

> PIONEER
> (turning back)
> Cornelius!

Sal stops in front of Pioneer as fire closes in from behind. Burning soot and ash lands in their hair and on their clothes. Sal brushes it off Pioneer.

> SAL
> I want to to find him too, but we
> have to keep moving.

EXT. CLEARING IN FOREST - SAME

The fire crackles and roars, sending forward scorching winds and raging black smoke. Cornelius looks wretched. Barely able to see in front of him, he scampers over and through the flaming mayhem. Without knowing it, he steps into a mud pot.

                CORNELIUS
    Ahhhhh!

He yanks his foot out and falls backward away from the bubbling water. It's turquoise blue and in places, it boils fiercely. He gets up, shakes his foot around, re-arranges his pack, then limps onward.

EXT. MOUNT SHERIDAN/HEART LAKE TRAIL FORK - DAY

Vicky and Scruffy hustle along a burnt path where the heat still packs a punch. They move with grim determination when they come to a paper stuck on a rock.

                VICKY
    Look girl, paper beats rock.

She picks it up as if she's cleaning trash. The paper's edges are singed like an old treasure map. A red line traces from the trailhead parking lot to Heart Lake and there's a red circle with "BEAR HABITAT" in her handwriting.

She hesitates, then continues on, stopping at the Mt. Sheridan/Heart Lake Trail sign. The only remaining letters are an h, an e, and an L. Both trail arrows point straight down.

                VICKY
    I think I know whose this is. How
    could they be out here?

Vicky closes her eyes for a moment and holds her head back. She takes a deep breath and thinks.

              VICKY (CONT'D)
     (compassionate)
    We should go find them.

She puts the map to Scruffy's nose who sniffs. Scruffy points into he woods towards the same path the deer and the three men aborted from the trail.

> VICKY (CONT'D)
> Okay, girl. Tu puedes hacerlo. Go
> get 'em.

Scruffy jumps straight into the off-trail smoldering woods with Vicky running after her.

EXT. LARGE PINE TREE - DAY

Pioneer and Sal stop under a large pine tree. Sal takes off his shoes and his feet are red and blistered all over.

Pioneer takes his knife out to mark the tree. It's already been marked, by his own knife.

> PIONEER
> Doggone it! We just went in a
> circle.

> SAL
> I thought a pioneer would be bet-
> ter at orienteering.

> PIONEER
> I can navigate with my heart if I
> have to.

> SAL
> At this rate, you couldn't find
> the Statue of Liberty in New York
> Harbor.

> PIONEER
> Fair enough. How about you answer
> a crossword? What's a nine-letter
> word for someone screwed?

Sal starts counting his fingers.

> SAL
> Incarcerated, incinerated,
> i...immolated.

> PIONEER
> Cornelius. The fire was on top of
> him.

Pioneer stops and stares down at a rock. He takes out
his canteen. He looks over at Sal, and then at Sal's
belt buckle.

> PIONEER (CONT'D)
> Take off your belt.

> SAL
> I'm not like that. I think that's
> more of an army thing.

Pioneer pours water from his canteen into a dent in the
rock.

> PIONEER
> The buckle. Take off your belt.

Sal whips the belt around his body and Pioneer snatches
it before Sal lets go. Pioneer smashes the pin on a
rock. Sal wrestles the belt back.

> SAL
> Are you insane? That's fine
> Corinthian leather.

Sal puts his belt back on and buckles it. The pin no
longer fits correctly and the belt hangs loosely.

> PIONEER
> We need a thin strip of metal.

Sal takes the pen from his pocket and hands the pen to
Pioneer who breaks off the clip and rubs it on his
pants. His hands shake. When he places it on the water's
surface, it floats unevenly and spins around.

> PIONEER
> It won't show us north.

Sal takes the ink reservoir out and chucks what's left
of the pen into the woods.

> SAL
>
> Cheap piece of crap. Probably
> wasn't even real metal.

> PIONEER
>
> I need a drink. Let's see if we
> can find an animal trail. It may
> lead to water.

Pioneer's eyes no longer glimmer and there's no more
smile. He reaches down to a patch of clover flowers and
dandelions, grabs a handful and eats then offers a bit
to Sal.

> PIONEER (CONT'D)
>
> Ya hungry yet?

As Sal puts his socks and shoes back on. He shakes his
head.

> PIONEER (CONT'D)
>
> Eat.

Sal takes a little and when they touch his tongue, he
gags.

> SAL
>
> I'm allergic to all non-deli
> food.

INT. RANGER PATRICK'S HOUSE - DAY

A TV in the background shows the park's evacuation.
Maria clutches the drapes at the front window. A tear
falls as she caresses her tummy and watches the dreary
fog of smoke and embers drift by.

INT./EXT. BUS - DAY

The small bus navigates down a road between two walls of
fire as flames buttress both sides, pummeling it. The
firefighters clutch their tools and whisper prayers.

EXT. YELLOWSTONE FOREST - DAY

Cornelius walks in a burned-out patch of trees. He senses someone in the darkness behind him. He spins and for a split second it looks like a person amid the smoke and shadows.

                    CORNELIUS
          Sal? Pioneer? Who's there?

The smoke clears. It's two burnt tree trunks whose black, stumpy arms reach out for a hug. Cornelius turns and marches onward.

EXT. UNMARKED TRAILHEAD - DAY

The bus pulls into a narrow pathway off-road, where a strand of trees opens up revealing a dirt path. Keezheekoni's crew exits the bus, loads up and heads onto a trail while forest fires CRACK and POP and smoke drifts through the trees.

EXT. YELLOWSTONE FOREST - DAY

Pioneer marks another pine tree with his knife.

Sal stops and stands up tall. He breathes and relaxes his body.

                    SAL
          Coffee pot's percolating.

Pioneer tugs his beard.

                    PIONEER
          Oh, okay. You have any mountain
          money?

Sal is confused. Pioneer sticks his hand in his pocket and pulls out a few squares of toilet paper.

                    PIONEER (CONT'D)
          Butt hanky. What we call it in
          the backwoods.

Sal takes a wad of twenties from his wallet.

> SAL
> I'll use this.
> (imitates Robin Leach)
> Lifestyles of the Rich and Fa-
> mous.

INT. HELICOPTER COCKPIT - DAY

Michael carefully pilots the craft, grasping onto the control stick with an iron grip. Duka squeezes himself in tight, holding on with one hand and with the other pointing to an expanse of burnt and burning forest next to Heart Lake.

> DUKA
> There's the northwest side of
> Heart Lake. Get lower.

Michael descends. Turbulence bashes them as they scan through a veil of smoke and flames. They lower and in-tense upsurges of wind buffet the craft. Michael tussles with the control knob.

> MICHAEL
> We can't get closer.

The windows are shrouded in thick smog.

> DUKA
> I can't see.

A strong updraft jolts the helicopter.

> MICHAEL
> We got to pull up.

Michael pulls the knob back. They rise.

> DUKA
> I'll call in the water bombs.

EXT. SKY - DAY

The helicopter turns West and flies above the fire
fronts where orange flames dance among blackened trees.

EXT. YELLOWSTONE FOREST - DAY

A crow watches Sal squat behind a tree when helicopter
blades SLAP overhead. They look up.

> SAL
> Now?

Pioneer waves his hands around and Sal pulls up his
shorts without buckling, then runs to an opening. He
waves with one arm and holds his shorts up with the
other.

> SAL AND PIONEER
> Help! Help!

Pioneer and Sal signal the aircraft. The helicopter
hangs there for a moment.

Sal reaches up with a vigorous two-hand wave. His khakis
drop to his ankles.

As the chopper pulls away behind a veil of smoke, Sal
rips off the belt and chucks it up at the helicopter.
The belt lands in a tree and lodges onto a branch.

The helicopter disappears. Sal pulls up his shorts.

Pioneer taps two fingers on an open hand with a dot dot
dot, dash dash dash, dot dot dot.

> PIONEER
> (said while tapping his hands)
> S...O...S.

> SAL
> You want to Save Our Sal. Give
> some of that mountain money.

After receiving a few squares, Sal retreats behind the
tree. The crow flies over to the branch where Sal's belt

hangs. It dislodges the pin with few pecks, then takes it in its beak and flies off.

EXT. YELLOWSTONE FOREST - TRAIL - DAY

Keezheekoni leads her crew, clad in bright yellow jackets, single file, down a slope, deep in the dark, drab forest. Headlamps bob along a narrow path surrounded by somber smoke clouds tinged by fires with an eerie red glow.

EXT. AIRPORT - DAY

Patrick and the six smokejumpers load themselves and their equipment onto a DH-6 series Twin Otter plane.

INT./EXT. RANGER PATRICK'S HOUSE - DAY

Maria sits in the living room on a sofa with one large suitcase and a smaller baby bag near her feet. She stares straight ahead, holding her stomach.

A knock at the door. She opens it to Patrick's parents, MATT, 60's, slightly bald, and CHRISTINE, 60's, graying hair.

                    CHRISTINE
          Maria, hi. How are you?

Maria nods.

                    CHRISTINE (CONT'D)
          Ready to go, dear?

Maria steps out into the arms of Christine. Matt dutifully grabs Maria's belongings.

INT./EXT. DH-6 TWIN OTTER - DAY

Jet engines BLAST as the plane rolls down the runway. Inside, the smokejumpers put on their parachutes. The plane lifts off the ground, wobbling and jolting the passengers.

                    PATRICK
          Looks like there's gonna' be
          turbulence. Hold onto your wigs.

EXT. FOREST MEADOW - DAY

Keezheekoni and the crew emerge from the woods on the
east side of the meadow. The glade is dark and sinister.

Angry gusts of hot air blast through the trees across
the open field, whip over the grass, sedges and flowers,
then clobber the firefighters with a drizzle of burning
ash.

                    KEEZHEEKONI
                (shielding her face)
          Cut a line from here to the
          trees. Two hundred feet long.

The firefighters spread out in a line, cutting and
slashing the Earth. In no time, they open up a swath in
the dirt between the meadow and the forest border.

A few firefighters ignite backfires with drip canisters,
burning the available tinder behind the developing
trench and up to the trees behind them. A few more
firefighters pump water on the leeward trees.

INT. SUPERINTENDENT DUKA'S OFFICE - DAY

Firefighters line up outside Duka's office. Cody is at
Duka's desk handing out an assignment folder to an older
firefighter.

                    CODY
          Have your men set up hoses and a
          perimeter around headquarters and
          the hospital tents. No one sleeps
          until this is over.

The firefighter leaves and the next one enters.

EXT. BISON MEADOW - DAY

Sal and Pioneer walk into an open meadow. Offshoots from

the fire front have ignited the tall grasses and trees. The men scamper over the non-burning ground, skirting the fires, and meet a hairy, horned behemoth.

The beast looks up at Sal. It stands amid the smoking detritus and a few boiling hot springs, framed by the flames in the trees behind it. Fires reflect off its bloodshot, eight ball eyes.

             SAL
    Woah! Let's go around.

Sal lowers his head as he and Pioneer skedaddle away. The animal king watches indifferently.

EXT. YELLOWSTONE FOREST - HILL - DAY

Scruffy sniffs as Vicky speeds along behind her. They go up the hill where Sal and Pioneer left Cornelius behind.

Scruffy smells the tree behind which Pioneer hid. She barks and they descend the other side, through the burning devastation.

EXT. YELLOWSTONE FOREST - DAY

A sweaty, dirty and drenched Cornelius plods along the littered and burning forest floor. With each gust of wind, red and yellow flames lash out at him, and a shower of sparks whizz by.

He arrives at a creek and runs in. He attempts to lie in the stream for refuge as the oncoming fire closes in from behind. The water is so shallow he can't get even halfway under so he flees upstream.

SPLISH, SPLASH, THUMP, THUMP.

He re-enters the woods, clamoring through an igniting forest full of flaming snags, litter and dead trees. He slashes through the lit deadfall, squeezing between branches and over logs, running headlong through the devil's obstacle course.

The fire behind Cornelius burns from the ground to the treetops. It rings in his ears as he scrambles forward avoiding as much of the burning as he possibly can.

The fire front catches him. Like a fire-breathing dragon about to pounce, it opens its mouth and blows. The flames jab him. He lunges forward and through the air with a desperate off-balance effort between some small trees, falling flat on his face.

BOOM.

> CORNELIUS
> God! Help!

Fire blows right at him and then over his head. Cornelius crawls away into the stand of small trees. The young, green trees surrounding him heat up, crackle and smoke, but do not burst into flames.

In this verdant oasis, Cornelius watches the sea of flames hopscotch over him. He lies amid the grove, stunned. A coat of perspiration and salt sticks to his clothing. He's covered with blisters and abrasions, his lips are cracked and bloody.

EXT. FOREST MEADOW - DAY

A rumbling arrives from across the meadow and behind the trees. It grows louder as the Snake River Complex fire arrives with its sharp flames and burning whips and launches firebrands at Keezheekoni and her anxious crew.

> KEEZHEEKONI
> Have emergency tents ready.

The wind HOWLS, and that quickly, everything is up in flames.

> KEEZHEEKONI (CONT'D)
> Hold the line!

The axe and shovel-wielding soldiers begin the battle. It's a warlike mayhem of dirt, metal, and flame. They stamp out blazes and shovel dirt onto incipient fires. In the madness, a PIPEMAN pumps water from the stream to douse spot fires.

INT. DH-6 TWIN OTTER - DAY

The smokejumpers sit inside the cargo area, clipped in, and waiting. The plane cuts through the dark sky and jolts up and down. They hold on tight.

When the flight smooths for a moment, Patrick stands to look out the open side door. He alerts the smokejumpers and they form a line against the wall. JEFFERSON, the lead smokejumper, 40s, African-American, moves in front of the open door.

> PATRICK
> Got this?

Jefferson scans out for a moment, turns, looks Patrick in the eyes and nods.

> PATRICK (CONT'D)
> The drop spot's East of the
> gulch.

Jefferson spread-eagles through the ether. In a moment a meandering line of men cut through the clouds.

EXT. YELLOWSTONE FOREST - DAY

Scruffy sniffs through the burnt debris of the forest. She turns to the right and walks a bit, turns to the left and tries that direction. She begins scouting in wider and wider circles.

Vicky shakes her head.

> VICKY
> Come here, girl.

Scruffy comes over.

> VICKY (CONT'D)
> Fire probably burned over the
> trail. Wanna' try again?

She takes out the map and puts it to Scruffy's nose. Scruffy sniffs, turns around, then spins back and sits.

EXT. FOREST MEADOW - DAY

In a dark, burning and smoky meadow, Keezheekoni and her
crew brandish their tools like the swords of medieval
knights. She runs up and down the line helping with
equipment and tasks, always where the fire threatens
most.

The pine trees, though sprayed with water, heat up,
crack and burn. The trees behind their line go up in
flames. One falls where the Pipeman sprays water on a
ground fire.

                    KEEZHEEKONI
               Look out!

Flaming branches crash around the Pipeman. Keezheekoni
lunges over and pulls him away and they tumble. A large
branch pins the man's leg. He struggles. Keezheekoni
yanks him out and jumps on him to extinguish his flaming
pants.

Fires are on both sides of the crew. They clutch their
fireproof tents. Keezheekoni looks to their rear. The
trail they arrived in is halfway razed.

                    KEEZHEEKONI (CONT'D)
               Retreat to the center of the
               meadow.

Keezheekoni and FIREFIGHTER ONE, an Asian in this 20s,
assist the Pipeman as they head to the safety of the
only un-burnt area.

EXT. YELLOWSTONE FOREST - DAY

Pioneer and Sal stop in the middle of the thick forest.

                    PIONEER
               I'm getting pretty thirsty and
               hungry.

                    SAL
               Me too.

                        PIONEER
          We can find berries, wild onions.

Pioneer brandishes the sharp end of his knife and points
over at a squirrel nibbling on a mushroom cap.

                     PIONEER (CONT'D)
          Or eat mushrooms.

Pioneer walks over and the squirrel scurries away chat-
tering. He plucks a few of the fungi.

                          SAL
          I wouldn't chance fate any more
          than you have to.

                        PIONEER
          See that squirrel up there? It
          just ate these and it ain't
          dyin'.

Pioneer tastes them and offers one to Sal.

                     PIONEER (CONT'D)
          Would cook real nice with some
          roasted squirrel, a little wine.

Sal takes it. He puts it up to his mouth. His hand quiv-
ers. When it touches his tongue, the saliva reacts and
he spits it out.

                          SAL
          I love Italian, however, I'll
          pass on the Squirrel Marsala.

EXT. YELLOWSTONE FOREST - HALO OF TREES - DAY

Fire paints a mosaic pattern of black on the forest,
which alternates between burned and unburned sections of
trees.

Cornelius sprawls on the pine needles in a green grove
of trees. Soot smears Cornelius' cheeks and his
whiskered chin.

A smoky fog swirls by, like phantoms in a funeral procession, then dissipates into the beyond where a pyre of older trees pop and sizzle.

Cornelius gets up and rummages in his pack for food.

Nothing.

He dumps the pack out. Empty bags of trail mix, candy wrappers, and a plastic bagel bag drop to the ground.

He reaches in the pack and pulls out a cookie tin. He opens it. Relief. There's one cookie left inside. He holds it for a moment in front of him.

> CORNELIUS
> Stomach, we're going on a fast.

He puts the cookie back in the tin, shoves the trash into his bag, then hikes out into the smoldering woods.

EXT. NORTH YELLOWSTONE WOODS - DAY

The smokejumpers appear out of the dark, obscured sky, guiding themselves down feet first into an opening in the trees. They touch down with a forcible impact. Then comes the deflating parachutes.

> PATRICK
> (wrapping his parachute)
> Perfect drop, boys.

A straggler, RED, 21, comes down and hits hard, twisting his ankle and leg. He gives Patrick a look of pain.

> RED
> It's not bad. I think I can walk.

> PATRICK
> You have to. Can't leave you.

Patrick breaks out a first aid kit and wraps his ankle as Jefferson wraps up Red's parachute. Red tries to get up. He falters.

                    PATRICK (CONT'D)
          Grab my arm.
               (to the smokejumpers)
          Let's take turns giving him a
          shoulder.

Patrick aids Red up and they head out.

EXT. FOREST MEADOW - DAY

Fiery bullets whizz through the air. Half the meadow and
all of the surrounding forest burns. Keezheekoni's dazed
crew collapses. Sweaty and dirty, their faces are black,
their eyes are red, and their noses are caked.

Keezheekoni and FIREFIGHTER TWO, 30s, tend to the hurt
Pipeman whose left leg and side torso are burnt. Over
his charred skin are thick splotches of blackened blood.

                    FIREFIGHTER ONE
          That was movin' thirty miles an
          hour!

                    FIREFIGHTER TWO
          We survived Firemageddon.

                    FIREFIGHTER ONE
          Never should've been in front of
          it.

                    KEEZHEEKONI
          Radio in a distress call.

A RADIO OPERATOR, female, late 30s, sets up the two-way.

                    RADIO OPERATOR
          Grant Village, do you read?

                    FIRE FIGHTING HQ (O.S.)
          Loud and clear.

                    RADIO OPERATOR
          Firefighter down. Request ren-
          dezvous forty-four degrees four
          minutes forty- seven.

INT. SUPERINTENDENT DUKA'S OFFICE - DAY

The radio call gets Duka's attention.

> RADIO OPERATOR (V.O.)
> ... point two seconds north, one
> hundred ten degrees, twenty-seven
> minutes twenty-seven point four
> seconds west.

> FIRE FIGHTING HQ (V.O.)
> Affirmative. Will send a 'copter.

Duka snatches the mic. There's an unnerving SCRATCH.

> DUKA
> This is John Duka. Was your mis-
> sion a success?

> RADIO OPERATOR (V.O.)
> Firebreak failed. One man down.

EXT. YELLOWSTONE FOREST - DAY

Scruffy runs ahead. She stops, sniffs a rock and points.
Vicky comes over and finds a discarded pen on the
ground. She examines it closely. There is a stamped
inscription of "Leibowitz and Constantini $5,000,000."

> VICKY
> Yup. This looks familiar.

Burning debris flies all around and winds whip the
flames. They move onward.

EXT. YELLOWSTONE FOREST - ANIMAL TRAIL - DAY

Sal fiddles and fidgets with small pieces of a stick in
his hand as he and Pioneer shuffle amid the blowing
smoke, across a meadow at an oblique angle to the left.
Tired and out of breath, their sweaty clothes cling to
their bodies.

They come to a bare area where a hot spring bubbles and
steams. A gigantic black snake warms itself on the dark

soil.

When Sal spies it, he jumps back. The snake returns Sal's alarmed gaze with a flick of the tongue.

>   SAL
>   (throwing small pieces of stick to the
>   ground)
>   You said the animal trail would
>   lead us to sweet ambrosia? That's
>   boiling and guarded by a giant
>   snake.

Pioneer looks over. The snake has partly shed a loose layer of its outer skin.

>   PIONEER
>   God damn it, you're right. I
>   messed up. But don't worry. It's
>   molting.

Pioneer sits down and puts his head down. Sal comes over and puts a hand on Pioneer's shoulder.

>   SAL
>   You all right?

Pioneer gazes up at the obscured heavens.

>   PIONEER
>   How can we get out? There's no
>   North Star. No sun, no moonshine.

>   SAL
>   You don't need any moonshine.
>   We're gonna make it out of here.

>   PIONEER
>   I wanna' beer. I'm good for it.
>   Five cents a can.

Sal looks concerned.

INT. BELL HUEY HELICOPTER - DAY

Keezheekoni's worn-out crew belts themselves in as

Firefighter Two straps the injured Pipeman onto a stretcher. The helicopter thumps and rises.

> PILOT
> There's no visibility. We have to head east over the divide.

> FIRE FIGHTING HQ (V.O.)
> (over radio)
> Roger that, Michael. 10-4.

EXT. PARK HEADQUARTERS - DAY

A group of five firefighters monitor the trees around the park headquarters and the two canvas tents. They are at the ready with hoses and firefighting equipment in hand.

EXT. YELLOWSTONE FOREST - DAY

Hot and ruddy, Cornelius wanders along as he hears the THUMP- THUMP-THUMP of helicopter blades.

A Bell Huey's lights pop out of the dark, misty stew of smoke. Cornelius throws off his pack and jumps up and down waving his arms back and forth.

> CORNELIUS
> Help! Help!

The helicopter doesn't slow, so Cornelius grabs a dirty cooking pan from his pack and tries to flash a signal, but there's no sun. Cornelius stands, waving the pan, unnoticed in the darkness. The chopper whirls away, out of sight.

EXT. FOREST - DAY

Scruffy darts ahead of Vicky into a forest opening. Scruffy goes behind a tree and barks. Vicky comes over. She covers her mouth.

> VICKY
> Ewww.

In the dirt, twenty-dollar bills are smeared with feces.

> VICKY (CONT'D)
> We got 'em.

Scruffy sniffs a little then points ahead, in the direction of fires.

> VICKY (CONT'D)
> We'll have to go around. Come on!

Vicky and Scruffy jog to the left through the woods amid the red burning coals and some low burning fires. Sal's belt, without the prong, sits on a branch in the tree above.

EXT. YELLOWSTONE WOODS - DAY

Cornelius is bathed in smoke as he walks along an animal path, exhausted. He meanders by dead branches and trees and various small fires scattered throughout the woods. Fire intensifies behind him and hurries him along.

He hits an intersection of about ten different paths that head in all directions.

He points his hand out guessing, divining which way the water will be. He stops his arm and points at a trail. He heads off in that direction, faster than the fires behind him.

INT. SUPERINTENDENT DUKA'S OFFICE - DAY

Inside Duka's office, reports and equipment are strewn about. Duka and Cody closely scrutinize a fire map.

> DUKA
> Almost half a million acres are
> on fire.

> CODY
> This fire's got us on our heels.

> DUKA
> I gotta' pull the trigger.

                    CODY
          Slurry bombs?

Duka nods as he picks up the radio.

                    DUKA
          Missoula Control Tower, this is
          Superintendent Duka. Can you get
          a DC-10 tanker with slurry over
          here?

                    MISSOULA AIRPORT DISPATCHER (V.O.)
          We have several loads on the
          ready. How much do we drop?

                    DUKA
          This is war. Give it all you got.

EXT. ELK MEADOW - DAY

Sal and Pioneer push through the forest understory of
vegetation and briars. Their arms and legs get cut and
scratched. A fire follows behind them. Sal takes off his
shoes for a look at his feet. They're blistered and
bloody.

                    SAL
               (exhausted)
          Let's get a quick rest.

He puts the shoes back on and they sit against some
lodgepole pine trees next to the grassy glade and close
their eyes.

It's quiet until some noise and movement in the trees
alerts Pioneer. His eyes reopen.

A group of elk walk out of the trees, into the field,
and forage in the grass, paying no notice to neither the
fires nor the men nearby.

Pioneer glances sideways at them.

                    PIONEER
               (quietly to Sal)
          Enemy troops.

Pioneer's eyes narrow. He reaches for his military knife.

                    PIONEER (CONT'D)
               (whispering)
          I'll circle behind.

Pioneer gets on all fours and slowly sneaks around the meadow. While chomping on clumps of grass, the elk look up intermittently at Pioneer. A few even reposition themselves, in order to face him more directly.

Pioneer creeps to within twenty-five feet of the elk, then mimics them by chewing on large tufts of grass.

Pioneer balances himself. He lifts his throwing arm and steadies the knife. He slowly inhales, then on the ex-hale he hurls the blade. It spins through the air and lands without ever making its mark. The elk bound away.

The pounding hooves awake Sal. He finds Pioneer with his head bowed down, vigorously chomping on the long blades of grass.

                    SAL
          Pioneer, it's time to go.

                    PIONEER
          I'm hungry.

Sal helps Pioneer up and then wraps his arm around Pioneer's shoulder.

                    SAL
          Your wife, Debra, right? She'll
          be so happy to see you she'll
          cook you a nice steak, mushrooms,
          beer, everything you like.

They hike off leaving Sal's blood soaked socks on the ground.

EXT. NORTH YELLOWSTONE FOREST - DAY

Patrick and the smokejumpers cut through some deadfall with saws and douse the last flames with dirt. He points

through the treetops where a large billowing plume
that's gathering smoke and heat.

> PATRICK
> That's the gulch fire. Head over
> that way toward that big cloud.

The men fall in line behind Patrick as Jefferson helps
Red along and they march off.

EXT. YELLOWSTONE PARK - TWO OCEAN PLATEAU - DAY

Cornelius limps and drags himself up an inclined slope.
When his shoe gets lodged in a root, he jerks and falls
forward, bracing himself on the ground with his hands.

> CORNELIUS
> Ow!

He unbinds his foot, in various states of imbalance, and
tries not to fall down the hill. He surmounts the south-
west plateau by grabbing a nearby tree branch and
pulling himself on top.

At 10,000 feet in elevation, he surveys the fires and
smoke that surround him. He takes the cookie from the
tin and holds it up like a compass.

> CORNELIUS (CONT'D)
> We're surrounded. Have to stay on
> the ridge and head East and go
> down before the fires converge.
> Yellowstone River's down there
> somewhere.

He looks at the cookie.

> CORNELIUS (CONT'D)
> Oh yeah, sorry about this.

He takes a small bite. A fierce gust of wind blows fire,
sparks and smoke up the slope.

                    CORNELIUS (CONT'D)
          Got to put you back. You smell
          good, but you've heard the horror
          stories of cookies getting
          burned.

He puts the cookie and tin away then limps forward on
tight, sore muscles.

EXT. NORTH YELLOWSTONE HILLSIDE - DAY

Patrick's team gathers on the side of a grassy hill,
scanning across the gulch for fire. At the bottom of the
slope, there's the warning of oncoming thick, dark
smoke.

                    PATRICK
          Red, stay here. The rest of you
          cross the hill.

The men move across carrying packs, Pulaskis, and cross-
cut saws. Flames arrive at the bottom. They keep moving.

A strong gale of wind pushes the fire uphill. It changes
to a smoky steam, boiling up the slope. They quicken the
pace.

Halfway across, the fire, burning like a banshee, appears from behind the smoke.

                    PATRICK (CONT'D)
          Drop everything but your tents.
          Get off! Now!

The men throw down their packs and tools, running up the
steep slope with Patrick at the rear as blazing fire
bucks toward them like a hundred burning broncos.

They reach a rock at the top, seconds before the fire.
They skirt around both sides of it in a mad scramble to
beat the flaming grass to the trees. The fire catches
them.

Burning smokejumpers leap into the trees at the top,
slapping fire from their clothes. The pants of an older
veteran firefighter, Smokejumper One, catch fire and he

rolls on the ground. He squelches his burning pants leaving a hole where his leg is bloody and blistered.

There's a blood-curdling SCREAM. The men look back. They rush towards Patrick but are thwarted by the flames.

Patrick staggers around the back of the rock. He pops up his emergency tent as fires surround him. On fire, he climbs into a cleft in the rock, engulfed in flames. He falls down onto the tent.

CRIES of unbearable agony haunt the air. The men turn away.

EXT. BLUEBERRY MEADOW - DAY

Sal and Pioneer step out of the brush where the grass and sedges reach the height of their hips, trudging through the quagmire. On the meadow's edge, they come to a patch of blueberries, plentiful and ripe.

> PIONEER
> I can ferment these. Make some
> blueberry wine.

Pioneer squats alongside the bushes and takes out an army tin. He is jittery. He licks his dried-out lips. He crushes berries and puts the guck in his military mess tin.

> SAL
> You had your last hurrah. Try to
> remember your wife and kids.

Pioneer holds the pan out to Sal.

> PIONEER
> My mouth's dry. Spit in this.

Pioneer's feet jiggle his legs up and down. Sal is concerned.

> SAL
> You okay? Your legs are going up
> and down like a sewing machine.

A DC-10 flies over. Pioneer looks up.

>   PIONEER
>   Are they friendly?

The plane opens a hatch. Out flies half a million gal-
lons of red-orange slurry.

>   PIONEER (CONT'D)
>   Agent Orange. Take cover!

Pioneer cowers. A fearful Sal grabs him.

>   SAL
>   They're fighting the fires. It's
>   one of ours.

Pioneer grabs his own leg, where he has numerous cuts.

>   PIONEER
>   They got me! I'm bleeding!

>   SAL
>   You're fine. The briars cut you.

Pioneer twitches and spasms. He swipes at phantasmal in-
sects in the air.

>   PIONEER
>   They got air superiority.

>   SAL
>   It's a mosquito.

>   PIONEER
>   (in Vietnamese)
>   Du má! It burns! It burns!

EXT. VIETNAM VILLAGE - DAY (DREAM)

Pioneer and a platoon of soldiers crouch in the grass in
a meadow. Gunfire comes at them from across the meadow.
They watch the forest and see nothing.

A Cheyenne helicopter zooms in from his right. The Captain is on the radio.

>   CAPTAIN
>   Give them the Hellfire.

A young woman is tied up and connected to Pioneer. Ropes tie two small children to her. The children hide behind her and hold her tight.

The Cheyenne helicopter draws in close then blasts a Hellfire missile. Pioneer and the platoon watch as the woods explodes into flames.

>   CAPTAIN (CONT'D)
>   Get those POW's outta here. Move
>   out. Now.

END DREAM

EXT. BLUEBERRY MEADOW - DAY

Sal is shaking Pioneer by the lapel. Pioneer opens his eyes.

>   SAL
>   What? Where?

>   PIONEER
>   Rome. It's burning.

Pioneer seizes. His limbs extend and his body goes rigid. All of a sudden, Pioneer's limbs jerk around uncontrollably. Sal recoils.

EXT. ELK MEADOW - DAY

Scruffy comes up to socks stained red sitting on pine needles. Scruffy sniffs and licks them. Vicky follows behind out of breath and sees the bloody socks.

>   VICKY
>   Good girl.

Vicky takes a reading on her compass then looks into the burning woods.

EXT. BLUEBERRY MEADOW - DAY

Sal sits with Pioneer.

> SAL
> Look at us. What are we doing out
> here? A city boy has no business
> being out here.

Pioneer groans as he comes out of the seizure. He is
groggy. Sal gently holds him and touches his face.

> SAL (CONT'D)
> (gently)
> Hey.

Pioneer looks up, dead tired. Sal hears fires closing in
and the meadow becomes a smoky battlefield.

> SAL (CONT'D)
> You need medical attention.

Pioneer nods, turns and pukes. Sal takes a shirt from
his pack and wipes the foamy spit from around Pioneer's
mouth.

> SAL (CONT'D)
> I'm gonna get you out.

Sal picks up Pioneer, and they head out.

EXT. PARK HEADQUARTERS - DAY

Outside the office, the crew of firefighters patrol
around the buildings; the field is abuzz with chaos.
This includes firefighters and an increased amount of
press - reporting live on the extensive damage.

A helicopter lands in the marked-off area. The doors
open and Keezheekoni jumps down and unloads a stretcher.
Two medics run out and intercept her on the grass. She
waves to them as they take off with the stretcher.

Keezheekoni turns towards the park headquarters. Behind
her, a red sun is smothered in clouds of scarlet shaded
smoke.

INT. SUPERINTENDENT DUKA'S OFFICE - DAY

In the messy office, Duka is on the edge of his seat with Cody in front of him. A tattered Keezheekoni enters.

>   DUKA
> You weren't successful?

>   KEEZHEEKONI
> The fire jumped over us. One man was injured bad.

>   DUKA
> Keep that quiet. There's a lot of press out there.

>   KEEZHEEKONI
> I can't tell a lie. I'd rather you find me a job that matters.

>   DUKA
> Too much dignity, eh? How about a rain dance? Or do a critical job in the Southeast park.

>   KEEZHEEKONI
> I know that area like the back of my hand.
>   DUKA
> That's why I'm sending you, to take care of a park service cabin.

>   KEEZHEEKONI
> I'll do this land honor.

>   DUKA
> Just spray the cabin with retardant. Get a mule packed and get going early.

>   KEEZHEEKONI
> I'll leave at dawn.

>   DUKA
> Go, quick, like deer. There's a
> fast moving fire out there.

Keezheekoni nods and is out the door. Duka throws his head back, shuts his eyes and sighs.

>   CODY
> That Injun has some set of Rocky
> Mountain oysters.

>   DUKA
> That's why I got rid of her be-
> fore the Secretary arrives.

EXT. YELLOWSTONE WOODS - DAY

The gulch fire has died down to scattered patches of red and glowing embers. The smokejumpers lower Patrick onto a makeshift stretcher. He is alive and the gruesome burns are bandaged and bloody.

Jefferson points at the map.

>   JEFFERSON
> We're going East to our ren-
> dezvous.

The smokejumpers nod.

>   JEFFERSON (CONT'D)
> Move out.

They lift the stretcher and head across the top of the burned and smoking gulch. Patrick groans with each step. Blood soaks through the leg bandages on Smokejumper One as he and Red limp along at the end of the line.

EXT. FOREST - DAY

Ahead of Vicky, Scruffy freezes, she raises a paw, her tail goes up, and she points her nose at the grass. Vicky finds it; a glob of puke swarmed by flies. She gags. Scruffy licks the vomit. Vicky grabs her collar and pulls her away.

EXT. BEAUTIFUL MEADOW - DAY

Sal marks a tree with a rock. Above that, ten feet in
the air, deep gashes cut through the bark and into the
tree. A dark amber sap oozes out and coagulates like
blood.

The meadow is perfect and untouched. It hasn't yet
caught fire and it's a pristine, pastoral beauty. Sal
hikes with Pioneer hanging on his shoulder along a trail
bordered by tall grasses and flowers.

EXT. CONTINENTAL DIVIDE - DAY

The day is dark as night. A cloud of billowing smoke
roils through the trees. Above a seated Cornelius, the
sun bleeds through the clouds. He slumps over his leg
and pulls on a tick attached to his calf.

                    CORNELIUS
          These things are impossible to
          get off.

The backpack is next to him. He takes out the tin, opens
it and removes the cookie then contemplating it.

                    CORNELIUS (CONT'D)
          I'll wait until I find water,
          hopefully the river down here
          somewhere.

EXT. WOODS NEAR HEART RIVER - DAY

Vicky and Scruffy get to the edge of the meadow; she
spots Sal struggling with Pioneer. She tilts her head,
half-smiles and half tears up.

Scruffy darts off. ARROUGH! RUFF!

Sal turns. Scruffy bounds toward him and Pioneer.
Scruffy puts her nose on Sal's leg, then bows down.

                    SAL
          Do I know you?

Vicky approaches. Sal looks at her, overwhelmed.

                    SAL (CONT'D)
          Hey! What are you doing here?

                    VICKY
          I should ask what you're doing?
          You don't have a permit to be
          here.

                    SAL
          So, if you didn't know we were
          out here, how'd you find us?

                    VICKY
          Scruffy.

                    SAL
          Pioneer's sick.

                    VICKY
          Who? What's going on?

                    SAL
          Pioneer, he had a seizure.

                    VICKY
          What about the other guy? Cor-
          nelius?

                    SAL
          Burned. Call for help.

                    VICKY
          I don't have my walkie-talkie.
          I was in a rush. I was focused on
          other things. I forgot it.

Sal's a little broken up.

                    SAL
          We got to get them help.

                    VICKY
          Your skin's scorched.

                        SAL
            A burning stick smacked me.

Sal takes a step toward Vicky with his palms out, going
in for a hug.

                        VICKY
            Not the time.

                        SAL (CONT'D)
            I'm glad you found us.

Vicky takes out a first aid kit.

                        VICKY (CONT'D)
                    (to Pioneer)
            Let me check you over.

                        PIONEER
                    (half-way moaning)
            I'm okay.

                        SAL
            Do you have any idea how to get
            out of here?

EXT. SMALL CREEK - DAY

Cornelius descends a hillside. At the bottom, he crosses
a marsh and bumps into a small creek.

                        CORNELIUS
            Yes! Time to celebrate.

He strides off into the stream. His legs cramp, he falls
in and lands on a kneecap.

                        CORNELIUS (CONT'D)
            Ow!

He gets to his feet in pain, and drinks from cupped
hands. He chokes and coughs, catches his breath and
drinks again.

Cornelius trudges out of the stream and lies on his
back. His forearms and hands turn blue with goose bumps
and he's shivering. He grabs his abdomen.

                    CORNELIUS (CONT'D)
          This must flow into the Yellow-
          stone.

A pained look contorts his face. He vomits.

EXT. YELLOWSTONE WOODS - NIGHT

Four smokejumpers, including Jefferson, carry Patrick's
stretcher by the light of their headlamps. In the background, the fiery hills frame their silhouettes. The
burned Smokejumper One and the injured Red hobble along
behind them.

EXT. YELLOWSTONE RIVER - WEST SIDE - NIGHT

Cornelius stumbles through the brush. His clothes, a
little bit loose, stick on a branch. He yanks free and
surges forward, coming through the thicket and stumbles
onto the western bank of the Yellowstone River. He's
elated.

He takes the cookie out and holds it in the air. He
dances, then spasms and cramps.

He gazes in the water as the deep, dark, heavy river
rolls in a steady clip downstream. White water splashes
up and over large rocks and around the thick jams of
clogged branches.

He hears the rumble of fires closing in on him through
the darkness. From the woods come firebrands, notices of
an impending doom.

The fires are converging on him. As their edges reach
towards him, he looks to the river as a means to escape.
He steps in awkwardly, then stumbles. The rushing water
sweeps him downriver.

Several yards down, he pulls to the shore gagging and
drags himself out.

                    CORNELIUS
               (coughing and spitting)
          You're kidding me. You gotta' be
          Mark Spitz to get across this.

Cornelius' wet body tightens. His clothes stick to his slightly less rounds sides. Burning bits fly by. He squats down on his backside to rest and puts his head down on his pack.

EXT. YELLOWSTONE WOODS - NIGHT

Sparks snap and pop in the wind. Fires burn randomly here and there. Ashes float by like gray snowflakes and the ground cover is burned to charcoal.

Smoke obscures the setting sun and the woods darken to the color of the blackened earth.

While Scruffy scouts around, Vicky leans back on a tree and lays Pioneer on her lap. Sal hands her a rolled-up shirt from his bag and she places it under Pioneer's head. Pioneer is awake, looking up at the trees.

> PIONEER
> I wanted to make a home out of these trees one day.

> SAL
> You will. Once we get out of this prison.

> PIONEER
> Long and straight trunks, no branches except at the top. Lodgepole trees are perfect for log cabins.

> VICKY
> (to Pioneer)
> Rest.

Scruffy comes back, circles, and lies next to Vicky. Vicky then takes out her notebook. Sal takes off his hat and removes the paper from under the sweatband. He writes.

> VICKY (CONT'D)
> So you're a literate cowboy? You writing poetry?

                    SAL
          Notes of personal importance.

Vicky opens her book and shows Sal. The page contains
labeled columns with rows and rows of numbers.

                    VICKY
          These are my notes. This research
          is the real reason I'm out here.

                    SAL
          Do you study trees? Animals?

                    VICKY
          Forestry. How fire affects soil
          and the regrowth of trees. For a
          PhD.

Sal picks up a pinecone.

                    SAL
          So you study these?

Sal puts the cone on top of his hat.

                    SAL (CONT'D)
              (imitating Dan Aykroyd)
          I am a Conehead.

Vicky doesn't respond.

                    SAL (CONT'D)
          Remember? Saturday Night Live?

                    VICKY
          No, I haven't watched TV in eight
          years.

Sal throws her the pinecone.

                    VICKY (CONT'D)
          A lodgepole pine cone. Resin cov-
          ers it and only melts over 140
          degrees.

                    SAL
          During fire?

                    VICKY
          Yes. And then little baby seeds
          fall out.

Vicky's eyes wander. She bites a cuticle.

                    SAL
          Is that bleeding?

                    VICKY
          Nervous habit.

                    SAL
          Is it painful?

Vicky nods. She picks up her water bottle and she now
fiddles with the lid, lifting the pull spout open and
pushing it closed.

                    VICKY
          I present a dissertation in two
          days. On the fire, soil, pine
          trees. If we get out of here,
          it'll give some hope after the
          devastation.

                    SAL
          We will. Let's play a game. How
          about truth or dare?

                    VICKY
          What is this? Middle school?

                    SAL
          It might calm you down.

                    VICKY
          Okay, but I'm more than a little
          apprehensive.

Vicky closes the pull spout, then squeezes the bottle.

> SAL
> You? Scared? You made it through
> a forest fire to save strangers?

Vicky's face remains stern.

> SAL (CONT'D)
> That took courage.

Vicky breathes in then holds it for a moment and swallows.

> VICKY
> So you tell the truth? No lies?

> SAL
> The truth and nothing but the
> truth, so help me God.

> VICKY
> You go. Truth.

> SAL
> What do you think of me?

Vicky unscrews the cap, then screws it back on.

> VICKY
> You have money. Think it makes
> you attractive. You joke around,
> but don't seem to take much re-
> sponsibility for what you say.

> SAL
> I wanted to hear all the good
> things.

> VICKY
> I like what I see, now. Helping
> Pioneer. Truth or dare?

> SAL
> Truth.

                    VICKY
          What do you think of me?

EXT. WOODS - DAY (SAL'S DAYDREAM)

Vicky dressed as a woods nymph skips through the forest
with a pitcher of water on a beautiful, sunny summer's
day. Sal watches her skip and prance right up to him.
She lifts the pitcher and...

EXT. YELLOWSTONE WOODS - NIGHT

Water splashes across Sal's head and face as Vicky
squirts her bottle at him. Sal snaps out of it, shaking
the water off his head.

                    VICKY
          What are you thinking about?

                    SAL
          Sorry, I got distracted.

                    VICKY
          I wanna' hear your answer?

                    SAL
          You're trying to succeed in a
          man's world on your terms. Try to
          look nice, but not use it to your
          advantage. So focused on work you
          couldn't see a great guy even if
          he was standing right in front of
          you.

                    VICKY
          Truth. When you look at me, what
          do you see?

                    SAL
          I'm not gonna' lie. I do have a
          fantasy life.

Vicky squirts Sal in the face again.

                    VICKY
I'm not an object of pleasure.

                    SAL
Sorry. That was wrong. You are
stressed out, though.

                    VICKY
It's my dissertation. I don't get
any support. I did three extra
years of my life for my advisor
just to get my thesis approved.

                    SAL
The defense is not as hard as you
think. I've spoken to a lot of
juries.

                    VICKY
This committee's all-male, ex-
lumberjacks and bull riders. My
own advisor said, "When it comes
to data, size matters," and the
Dean thinks a woman should be
cooking and cleaning, not con-
tributing to science.

                    SAL
That's not fair.

                    VICKY
I'm not like the people from
around here. I'm a Latina from
California. All my family were
migrants. We picked in apple and
peach orchards, and cherry trees.

                    SAL
We're all immigrants.

                    VICKY
I changed schools a lot and I
managed to got into college, but
they don't think I'm capable.

> SAL
> I was laid off from a law firm by
> the same old, white Republicans
> in charge. Worked like a slave
> for them, seventy-five hours a
> week.

> VICKY
> This is the biggest thing I've
> ever done.

> SAL
> You can do it. Pioneer and I know
> you make a difference.

Vicky takes a deep breath.

> VICKY
> Thanks.

Sal looks at her waiting for a sign.

> VICKY (CONT'D)
> Time to rest.

Vicky gets comfortable. Sal tips his hat to her and
water drips from the rim. Embarrassed, he does a Michael
Jackson dance step and strikes a pose like in the music
video.

> SAL
> Who's bad?

> VICKY
> Stop. Those moves are ruining
> Michael Jackson for me.

> SAL
> I'm white. These hips don't move
> and I have no rhythm.

EXT. HEART RIVER - MORNING

A GRIZZLY BEAR saunters through the woods while glutting
itself on sub-alpine herbs, roots, and berries. It gets

to the river and enters, slurping and sucking in water. Then it lies in the water, intermittently scanning around.

EXT. YELLOWSTONE RIVER - DAY

Cornelius awakes on his side with his head on his backpack. He lifts himself up and immediately checks for his precious baked treat. It's still in his hand. He looks at it. He is about to nibble off a bite, but restrains himself.

Fires surround him on all sides except the river. Cornelius gets up and lumbers along the riverbank, holding the cookie carefully.

EXT. MEADOW/HEART RIVER - DAY

Sal, Vicky, Pioneer and Scruffy cross a stunningly beautiful meadow. They meander through a sea of flowers, grass, and sedges bordered on both sides by a verdant pine tree forest. In the distance, a giant rock rests on a grassy hillside.

A breeze blows from behind, flapping Sal's shirt collar.

EXT. YELLOWSTONE RIVER - CABIN CREEK TRAIL - DAY

Keezheekoni maneuvers the pack mule, across to the East side of the Yellowstone River. Fires approach the forest on the West. She and the mule find the trail. She grabs her gear and they bolt down the path, disappearing into the woods.

EXT. MEADOW/HEART RIVER - DAY

The grizzly exits the river as a faint breeze reaches the foraging bear. Its head lifts, nostrils flare and ears twitch. It sniffs. Instinctively, its mouth curls, exposing a fierce set of canines.

EXT. YELLOWSTONE RIVER - WEST SIDE - DAY

Cornelius limps along the river's edge. As sparks and thick clouds of smoke churn by him, the thin strands of muscles tighten up on the bottoms of his feet and they cramp.

                    CORNELIUS (CONT'D)
          Ow! Ow! Foot cramp.

He drops to the ground and grabs his foot. The sole is a tightrope of bunched-up muscle threads.

                    CORNELIUS (CONT'D)
          God, help, please.

The smoke around him rises with his plea.

INT. HELICOPTER - DAY - MOVING

In the bay of the Bell Huey, the smokejumper crew watch on as an EMT, 30s, female, stabilizes Patrick on a stretcher. Patrick moans at the EMT's slightest touch. She checks his airways. He's barely breathing.

                    EMT
          We're losing him.

                    HELICOPTER PILOT (O.S.)
          We can make it to the hospital
          tent at Park headquarters.

Patrick's head rolls to the side. He gurgles.

                    EMT
          Do it.

The chopper's nose turns west and dips. The pilot lowers the boom on the thrust.

EXT. CABIN CREEK TRAIL - DAY

Keezheekoni stomps down on her right foot. The black boot jams into the ground. She sprays a jet blast of fire repellent over the Park Service cabin with what resembles dry, lumpy shaving cream, covering the walls and roof.

EXT. MEADOW/HEART RIVER - DAY

Vicky, Sal and Pioneer pass by a large pile of loose scat.

After they walk by, Scruffy stops and sniffs the large mound of stool.

The three hikers enter the timberland and lope down a woody trail, shuffling along, carefully balancing Pioneer's 110 pounds.

Their heads are down, lost in concentration. They don't notice the grizzly, rising up in front of them with all its fearsome bulk.

The bear ROARS.

They are dangerously close. Sal steps in front of Vicky and Pioneer. Scruffy runs up barking. Sal holds Scruffy behind him with one hand and shields Vicky and Pioneer with the other.

Vicky slowly grabs Scruffy's collar.

> SAL
> (trying to remain calm)
> Get back!

Vicky retreats with Pioneer, all the while waving a hand in the air.

> VICKY
> Hey, bear. We're moving back.
> We're moving back.

Sal's eyes widen. The bear's gaze fixes on Sal's alarmed stare. Sal goes a starchy white. His hair stands on end.

The grizzly squints and sniffs the wind then wriggles its nose.

It stabs the air with its paws and stretches out its neck. It lets out a blood-curdling ROAR then drops its head and charges Sal with a rapid, fluid motion.

Adrenaline blasts into Sal's feet.

                    SAL
          Yaaahhh!!!

Sal runs, veering into the woods. The bear chases.

Sal scurries through a gauntlet of forest litter, brush, and trees. He jumps over downed timber and falls.

The bear gets to within twenty feet of him and stops, turns around and retreats a bit, only to spin and face him again. It emits another growl then puts its head down and charges one more time, crashing through the underbrush.

Sal is up and reaches the stream. He shimmies up a low branch on an aspen tree, smacking his watch hard in the process. The band breaks as Sal locks one leg on a branch and thrusts himself up. The other leg dangles.

The bear lunges and swipes. Sal lifts his leg up. The bear's catcher's mitt-sized paw catches the trunk below his feet and slams into it with a thud. Its claw rips through the bark. Sal scampers higher. The watch falls.

The bear digs both sets of claws in deeply and pulls itself up until its claws bear its body weight. Its grip softens, and it tumbles down, scratching the thin bark as it drops.

The bear goes berserk on the tree, letting loose so much fury that the aspen quakes. Sal digs his feet into the trunk and holds the branches tight. The tree tilts in the soil. The bear pushes within more violent thrust leaning into it with all its weight. The roots pop. The tree leans.

SMASH, BOOM, CRACK.

The tree keels over and collides with its neighbor. The branches hit with a vicious slap that jolts Sal from his perch. He falls, grabbing at the intertwining limbs. The bear pounces. Its paw grazes the bottom of his shoe. The shoe goes flying.

WOOF!

Scruffy chomps on the bear's haunches.

> VICKY
> Scruffy! No!

The bear spins to counter-attack. Scruffy maneuvers out of the way. The bear chases. Scruffy darts off. The bear looks at them and scents them. It scampers away.

Vicky watches the bear tread off into the woods. She heads over to Sal. He's shook up.

> VICKY (CONT'D)
> Let's go! This way!

Sal slides down the trunk. He straightens his shorts and shirt. He finds his shoe and puts it on. There's a hole in the sole. They run away in the opposite direction to the bear, along the side of the river.

A crow alights in the riverside aspen. Its beak aims down at the dull glimmer of Sal's watch. It flutters down, sneaks over, snatches the metal band and flies off.

INT. SUPERINTENDENT DUKA'S OFFICE - DAY

The office has been completely turned upside down. Duka watches out his window. His eyes narrow and his eyebrows furrow. He jerks up straight.

Duka's POV - A black SUV approaches. SECRETARY KENDALL, 60s, African-American, steps out of a government SUV and stands up dignified and strong.

Behind him, a helicopter lands, and two MEDICS, 30s, run out under the whipping wind of the spinning blades. The chopper door opens and a stretcher sticks out. The medics pull it down, then turn around and run the gurney across the grass.

EXT. PARK OFFICE - DAY

Fully equipped firefighters are on guard on both sides
of the building. The press, like a pack of hounds, await
Secretary Kendall who approaches the office steps.

                    ANN MARANEK
          Secretary Kendall, what can you
          tell us about the injured fire-
          fighter?

Behind Ann, the stretcher enters the med tent.

                    KENDALL
          We're public servants. This can
          put our men and women in harm's
          way.

                    ANN MARANEK
          Any word on his condition?

                    KENDALL
          The medical staff will give him
          complete, immediate care.

                    ANN MARANEK
          Are the fires a threat to the
          people in this area?

                    KENDALL
          Many capable crews are out there
          protecting people and property.

                    ANN MARANEK
          Are you able to contain the
          fires?

                    KENDALL
          No one can predict the wind, its
          direction, or how fast the fires
          will burn.

                    ANN MARANEK
          How long will the fire fighting
          take?

>   KENDALL
>   Rest assured we'll take care of
>   the park. If you'll please excuse
>   me, we have a lot to do.

He makes his move to get away and walks up to the trailer. As he opens the door, Maranek turns to the camera.

>   ANN MARANEK
>   At least one firefighter has been
>   injured...

EXT. YELLOWSTONE RIVER - DAY

The fire arrives. Cornelius gasps as the fire takes away the oxygen and his lungs heave and spasm. The popping, rip-snorting fire rings in his ears. Chunks and embers strike him, bouncing off his body as he scrambles over burning debris.

Cornelius is so weakened that he loses focus and tumbles, falls forward and hits his head on a rock. He lies there with the cookie in his hand and his pack on top of him. He writhes, GRUNTS, then passes out.

Trees torch, illuminating the dark sky. The firelight reflects in the water like a thousand tiny mirrors. A surge of hot air pushes over him and with it blackened, burning pine needles and sticks, covering him like a sackcloth.

The fire is less than one hundred feet away. Cornelius lies on the ground. His heart thumps. BA-BOOM. His body spasms. His eyes dart around behind his closed lids.

EXT. YELLOWSTONE RIVER - WEST SIDE - DAY (DREAM)

The house-sized, black-booted foot of Death marches through the woods.

BA-BOOM. BA-BOOM.

It's enormous and terrifying. It plants down on the trees across the river, smashing everything to bits.

BA-BOOM.

Death raises its foot again. Cornelius sees its sole.
There are trees, animals, and humans smooshed and
smeared all over it. Cornelius tries to get to his feet.
He can't move. Roots tie him to the ground.

He screams in horror.

EXT. HEART RIVER - DAY

Vicky, Sal, Pioneer and Scruffy look down Heart River.
It's surrounded by trees that are all on fire. Behind
them, the fires close in. Sal turns his body away from
the forest, flinching from the blistering heat.

> SAL
> (in a panic)
> Which way?

> VICKY
> This part of the forest is a tin-
> derbox. Get in the water.

Sal watches a tree crash into the river downstream.

> SAL
> You sure?

The flaming tree burns, hanging inches over the water.
Vicky looks back and forth in all directions. She turns
to Scruffy and shoots the dog a look of concerned confu-
sion.

> VICKY
> Which way?

Scruffy looks at the river and barks.

> VICKY (CONT'D)
> Help me.

Sal hesitates. Vicky pulls him toward Pioneer. They both
hold an arm, hobble into the river and help guide Pioneer in.

Scruffy jumps in and dog paddles to them. They lie back,

drifting down toward what may be their cremation.

INT. SUPERINTENDENT DUKA'S OFFICE - DAY

Secretary Kendall squeezes through the crowded office. He puts a briefcase on Duka's desk. It has a brass label and a combination lock with the inscription *Secretary Robert Kendall: Department of the Interior.*

> DUKA
> Mr. Secretary.

> KENDALL
> What are you doing risking lives?
> The press is roasting us!

> DUKA
> We're protecting the park, people
> and property at all costs.

> KENDALL
> That cost is in the millions!

> DUKA
> Everything's under control.

> KENDALL
> A man just came in on a stretch-
> er!

> DUKA
> These men would do anything for
> this park. They know the risks.

> KENDALL
> I came over two thousand miles
> for a briefing and it better be
> good.

EXT. HEART RIVER - DAY

As Sal, Vicky, Pioneer and Scruffy float down the river, burning branches crack, snap off, and drop, hissing as they hit the water. Winds whip burning chunks into the air.

Tree after tree fall into the river in front of them and behind them.

Sal and Vicky watch as directly ahead one more burning tree falls in.

>   VICKY
>   (to Sal and Pioneer)
>   Take a breath and go under.

They submerge themselves and swim under. Even Scruffy knows to dive beneath as far as she can. On the other side, Scruffy is the first one to pop up with paddling legs, then come the rest, coughing and gasping for air.

On the other side of the burning, they float down to Heart Lake where they get out of the river. Pioneer is awake, though groggy and slow.

>   PIONEER
>   Holy Moses!

Pioneer flops down. Sal immediately takes off his shoes.

>   SAL
>   Attacked by a fricking grizzly,
>   float down a tunnel of fire, un-
>   der a burning bridge. And saved
>   by an amazing dog and ranger!

They catch their breath.

>   VICKY
>   You were brave, too.

Sal's face blushes under the dirt and soot.

>   SAL
>   The part with the bear when I
>   screamed like a teenage girl?

>   VICKY
>   Shielding Scruffy and us from the
>   bear.

>   SAL
> I couldn't let it eat us. It's
> against the law to feed the ani-
> mals.

>   VICKY
> Now I know you're fine.

Sal rubs his blistered feet.

>   SAL
>   (imitating Howard Cosell)
> The thrill of victory and the
> agony of da feet.

Scruffy nudges Sal. He reaches down toward her. She lets
him pet her.

>   SAL (CONT'D)
> You brave, amazing dog.

Scruffy smiles then licks Sal's face.

>   SAL (CONT'D)
> And your breath stinks to high
> hell.

>   VICKY
> Maybe that's because you and Gre-
> tel here left a trail of crap,
> blood, and puke for us to follow.

Sal grabs a cloth from his pack and washes Pioneer's
face. Vicky notices this gesture. Pioneer then puts an
arm around Sal's shoulder and hugs him. Vicky has a
small spark in her eyes and a slight smile.

>   PIONEER
>   (tearful)
> I owe my life to you two.

Sal motions Vicky over. He then side-hugs Vicky and she
allows it.

>   SAL
> Wait a sec. My watch!

                         VICKY
          Really? How about your life?

                          SAL
          It was a Rolex!

                         VICKY
          You can get another one.

Sal takes a few steps back towards where they came from.
Vicky points to the northeast.

                     VICKY (CONT'D)
          Roosevelt Highway's this way.

She grabs Sal arm and turns him around. She pulls him
back with her to Pioneer. Sal is surprised and leaves
the watch behind to gladly follow her every move.

EXT. TEMPORARY HOSPITAL TENT - ICU - DAY

Patrick lies silent. His vital signs are touch and go.
Julie checks the IV lines as the monitors blink and
BEEP. His face and shoulders are burnt, and his eyelids
are swollen shut.

EXT. YELLOWSTONE RIVER - EAST SIDE - DAY

Keezheekoni reaches the river, still in her face mask.
She sees something in her periphery so she slows and
squints through the smoke and haze. Across the river, a
person, covered in ash, is trapped by the fire.

She drops the reigns of the mule and jumps in.

EXT. YELLOWSTONE RIVER - WEST SIDE - DAY (DAYDREAM)

Cornelius is laid out in the darkness. The black-robed
giant phantom of Death marches closer and closer to him.
Cornelius whimpers and spasms.

BA-BOOM.

Fear freezes Cornelius solid.

EXT. YELLOWSTONE RIVER - WEST SIDE - DAY

Fire reflects in Keezheekoni's mask. She turns Cornelius over then checks for a pulse. She hears nothing. She listens to his chest. She hears nothing. She pinches him. She watches closely, but sees no response.

EXT. YELLOWSTONE RIVER - WEST SIDE - DAY (DAYDREAM)

BOOM.

Death's boot is about to drop then Cornelius sees a light penetrating through the dark.

EXT. YELLOWSTONE RIVER - WEST SIDE - DAY

Keezheekoni holds Cornelius' eyelid open and shines her headlamp directly on his pupil. The tiny pupil doesn't react. She lets go of his eyelid, sits him up, yanks off his soot-covered pack, then lifts his bulk up onto her shoulders.

The fire roars, generating an immense updraft and the blast knocks into them and pushes them back a step.

Keezheekoni stares over at the giant wall of flames. A sudden wind gust thwarts the outward burst of flames.

She drags him into the river. As they tread into the current, the cookie, still in his hand, dissolves.

EXT. YELLOWSTONE RIVER - UNDERWATER - DAY

Keezheekoni's boots grab the sandy bottom. She digs the toe of her shoe in and begins to traverse. The current is too powerful. It pushes her feet backward, sweeping her off the bottom. The river carries them downstream.

EXT. YELLOWSTONE RIVER - DAY

The water whooshes them around. Keezheekoni turns Cornelius on his back and navigates them through the rapids and by rocks and snagged trees.

Keezheekoni breaststrokes with one arm and holds Cornelius with the other. She propels them with leg kicks. She exhales and the currents dunk them. She fights back to the surface.

Closer to the riverbank, Keezheekoni reaches her toes to the sandy river bottom. She holds on tenuously. The rippling current pushes around them. She muscles Cornelius on shore.

Keezheekoni steps behind Cornelius' cold body, puts him between her legs and hugs him closely. She rubs his bluish limbs. She listens to his breath. She hears a faint BOOM.

Cornelius opens his eyes.

On the other side of the river, a mayhem of fire knocks down trees. Cornelius' backpack goes up in flames.

INT. PARK HEADQUARTERS - HOSPITAL TENT - DAY

The heart monitor BEEPS. Maria holds Patrick's stiff hand, bandaged with an IV. She sobs. Patrick's parents are in the background.

Patrick coughs and gurgles through the respirator, fighting for his life. Julie administers a shot. Dr. Young scans Patrick's barely-open eyes. They ooze with pus.

                    DR. YOUNG
          Maria, you're going to have to
          leave.

Dr. Young motions to Julie who walks out a distraught Maria.

EXT. PARK HEADQUARTERS - DAY

A truck drops off Sal, Pioneer, Vicky and Scruffy at the hospital tent. Two medics rush over with a wheelchair and sit Pioneer down. Sal follows the medics and Vicky heads to the park office where a throng of press hovers outside.

INT. SUPERINTENDENT DUKA'S OFFICE - DAY

Duka sits grimly while Kendall paces in thought. Cody sits at his desk wading through the papers that have amassed in front of him.

Vicky enters.

> DUKA
> Vicky! You're back!

> CODY
> Thank God you're OK.

> VICKY
> Thanks. I'm sorry. I went out to do research and got caught in the blazes.

> DUKA
> You should never have been out there. Patrick David came back today, in the horizontal mode.

> VICKY
> Oh my God. How bad?

> DUKA
> He's on life support.

> VICKY
> I discovered two hikers were lost in the fires.

> DUKA
> What? I thought we eliminated backcountry permits two days ago?

> VICKY
> I found them, a park visitor and Pioneer.

> DUKA
> The vagrant?

                    KENDALL
          It was lucky you found them.
          Thanks for your service, ranger.

                    VICKY
          There's another guy still out
          there. A hiker, Cornelius Hedges.

Secretary Kendall glares at Duka who now grinds his
teeth.

                    DUKA
          Do you have any info on his
          whereabouts?

                    VICKY
          They lost him near the Mount
          Sheridan and Heart Lake trail
          juncture. He was engulfed in
          flames.
                    KENDALL
          Does the press know about this?

                    VICKY
          No. Only you. I can bring Scruffy
          out and do a search.

                    DUKA
          There's a boatload of burning out
          there. It'll be way too hard to
          scent.

Duka looks at Kendall and turns toward Cody.

                    DUKA (CONT'D)
          Send the fire crew outside on
          search and rescue for this guy,
          immediately.

INT. PARK HEADQUARTERS HOSPITAL TENT - DAY

Sal, with a bandaged cheek, sits at Pioneer's bedside.
Dr. Young, in a white lab coat, talks into a recorder.
Julie stands at the bedside taking Pioneer's pulse.

                    DR. YOUNG
     BP 75 over 70. No acute injuries.

                    SAL
     That's true. It's pretty ugly and
     it hurts just to look at him.

Dr. Young gives Sal a deadpan gaze then turns back to
his patient.

                    DR. YOUNG
     Pioneer, you had a seizure. You
     okay?

Pioneer opens his eyes and smiles.

                    PIONEER
     Best hand of three-card stud I
     ever had. Pair of queens and a
     king.

EXT. HEART LAKE TRAILHEAD PARKING LOT - DAY

A search party of dogs and men inspect the wreckage.
They find the cars covered in soot with melted tires and
busted windows. In Sal's back seat, the Playboy is half
ashes.

The team walks by the Heart Lake trailhead sign. It's
burned and missing Smokey the Bear's head. They walk by
it and go off into the woods.

INT. SUPERINTENDENT DUKA'S OFFICE - DAY

Secretary Kendall sits opposite Duka again, this time
more in his face. The fire map is between them. Kendall
presses both of his fists down on the map and raises
himself up over Duka.

                    KENDALL
     Half the park's on fire and the
     press is calling me "Barbecue
     Bob".

A sweat bead drips down Duka's face.

                    DUKA
          I did everything I could. There's
          never been fires this big.

                    KENDALL
          You have the American military
          behind you for God's sake.

The radio crackles to life:

                    KEEZHEEKONI (V.O.)
          Michael, this is Ranger
          Keezheekoni, do you read?

After a brief pause, a fuzzy transmission:

                    HELICOPTER PILOT (V.O.)
          Roger that, Keezheekoni. This is
          Michael, over!

                    KEEZHEEKONI (V.O.)
          Rescued victim near Yellowstone
          River. Need medical evacuation.

                    KENDALL
             (to Duka)
          The lost hiker.

                    DUKA
          Awesome!

                    CODY
          Yes!

A relieved Duka wilts into his chair.

                    HELICOPTER PILOT (V.O.)
          I'll get clearance. What's your
          twenty?

                    KEEZHEEKONI (V.O.)
          Half a mile southwest of Cabin
          Creek. Eastern side of Yellow-
          stone River.

Secretary Kendall grabs the mic.

> KENDALL
> This is Secretary Robert Kendall.
> Immediate clearance is granted.

> HELICOPTER PILOT (V.O.)
> Roger that, sir. Hang tight,
> Keezheekoni. ETA, five to seven.

The radio pops. Kendall glares at Duka.

> KENDALL
> What is another ranger doing out
> there alone?

> DUKA
> Protecting a Park Service cabin,
> from oncoming fire.

> KENDALL
> You should have never put her in
> harm's way if it isn't necessary.

> DUKA
> That Indian begged me for the
> job. She thought the Spirits of
> her ancestors would protect her.

> KENDALL
> Bigotry is never welcome in the
> Department of the Interior.

EXT. PARK HEADQUARTERS - DAY

Fire ignites the trees next to the parking lot. Burning red missiles fly through the air and land on and behind the park headquarters and hospital tents. The fire crew that had been protecting the buildings is no longer on guard and the structures ignite.

As the fire builds up and over the buildings, Duka and Kendall exit frantically. Duka and Cody grab the hoses set up outside and spray the hospital tents.

As the large tent goes up, a medical evacuation is already in progress. In no time doctors and nurses roll out Patrick, Pioneer, Sal, Maria and the other injured firefighters. Kendall runs over to Doctor Young and helps them run the gurneys to the parking lot.

> DR. YOUNG
> Get everyone out.

Despite Duka and Cody spraying the hospital tents, they go completely up in flames. They join the evacuees in the parking lot.

Patrick's heart monitor flat lines. Medics and STAFF surround him, rip back the sheet, hook up the defibrillator, and administer CPR. Maria runs over crying.

The doctors and nurses stop. Dr. Young whispers in Maria's right ear.

Maria falls on her knees in the grass and grabs her hair, screaming as if someone bashed in her skull. Julie and Nurse One come to her side to hold her as she thrashes and wails.

A watery fluid tinged with blood drips from Maria's pant cuffs onto the grass. Maria stops.

> MARIA
> My water!

She passes out in the nurse's arms.

> DR. YOUNG
> Lay her down on the grass. Get
> towels and a forceps.

EXT. YELLOWSTONE RIVER - EAST SIDE - DAY

The rotors THUMP. Keezheekoni buckles Cornelius in. The machine lifts off the ground as the tree limbs wave up and down. The chopper ascends, pushed sideways by the buttressing force of the firestorm's winds.

The helicopter spins around then lifts. The pilot points the chopper downriver, and heads off as the forest fires burn over the crest of the Absaroka Mountains, through the valleys and right up the river bank.

EXT. HEART LAKE/ MT. SHERIDAN TRAIL JUNCTURE - DAY

A search party of dogs and men spread out in a line and walk through the burnt woods. Flashlights shine every which way.

The search party stops at the trail juncture when a radio call comes in. The lead man picks up his walkie.

> KENDALL (V.O.)
> Call off the party.

The lead search man whistles out loud. He then hand-signals everyone to wrap it up and head back to base.

INT./EXT. OLD FAITHFUL LODGE - OFFICE - DAY

A stretcher is taken from a chopper and medics whisk Cornelius to Old Faithful Lodge. Inside, the hotel is set up as a makeshift emergency center.

In the office, Duka sits at a desk. In front of him, Secretary Kendall stretches himself out, towering over Duka.

> KENDALL
> You weren't ready for this type
> of emergency.

> DUKA
> I followed the park's procedures
> on fire fighting. Lightning
> started eighteen fires which I
> had to let burn. I thought they
> would eventually die out.

Kendall is unmoved by Duka's plea.

> DUKA (CONT'D)
> And I protected all human life
> and property.

                    KENDALL
          A ranger died, two park service
          women were in the fires, and
          three visitors were lost. Your
          own headquarters and hospital
          tent burned down which by the way
          could have killed a number of
          doctors, nurses, and patients.

                    DUKA
          I'll have you know I searched for
          Vicky personally.

                    KENDALL
          Good thing you didn't find her.
          She rescued two park guests.

Kendall stares Duka down.

                    DUKA
          I had to send in smokejumpers.
          The fires would have been deadly
          to the lumber industry.

                    KENDALL
          Human life is as valuable as all
          that timber.

                    DUKA
          I dedicated thirty-five years of
          my life to this park.

                    KENDALL
          It's time to find a warm place
          and retire.

                    DUKA
          I hate the heat. That's why I'm
          in Wyoming.

                    KENDALL
          Look at the good side. At least
          you won't have to clean out your
          office.

Duka storms out.

                    KENDALL (CONT'D)
          Deputy? I need your help.

     Cody looks up with hopeful eagerness.

                    CODY
          I'd be honored, sir.

                    KENDALL
          Tell me about the ranger that
          just called in. I sense she cares
          a lot about this park.

     Cody gets a file and hands it to Kendall.

                    KENDALL (CONT'D)
          She had the highest scores in the
          firefighter academy. There's a
          strong background in biology. She
          spent seven straight winters
          here, and is a local Native.

                    CODY
          If I may speak sir. She's green
          and doesn't follow command.

                    KENDALL
          She saved a hiker. I see a Native
          American woman and bona fide
          hero.

     INT. OLD FAITHFUL LODGE - LOBBY - DAY

     A dozen park employees sit quietly in the waiting area,
     mourning Patrick and comforting one another. Vicky and
     Sal sit alone, off to the side.

                    SAL
          You saved me from death row.

                    VICKY
          Thanks. It's nice to be acknowl-
          edged.

                    SAL
          When I was running from the fire,
          lost, I realized something.

Sal looks down and to the left, remembering.

                    SAL (CONT'D)
          When we met in the ranger office,
          sorry for being a jerk.

                    VICKY
          Is that humility? How attractive.

                    SAL
          I'm impulsive, which can get
          me into trouble. I'm actually
          a better person than people
          think.

                    VICKY
          I saw that. With Pioneer and the
          bear.

Sal looks into her eyes.

                    SAL
          I was wondering, how did you know
          we were out there?

                    VICKY
          I found your park map. Was pretty
          sure you needed help. Cornelius
          being overweight, you a fish out
          of water, so I put Scruffy on the
          scent. Maybe I thought I'd be in
          less trouble for being out there
          if I found you.

                    SAL
          Someday I'll save someone from
          something bad.

Vicky looks at Sal with empathy.

> SAL (CONT'D)
> (imitating George Bush)
> I want a kinder, gentler me.

Their eyes connect. The spark comes back and Vicky smiles.

> SAL (CONT'D)
> We experienced life, death, and
> birth together.

> VICKY
> I'll be up all night so I can
> prepare for my dissertation to-
> morrow. Truthfully, I don't know
> if I can do it.

> SAL
> If you can defend yourself from a
> jerk, a bear, a fire, you'll be
> okay on that defense.

> VICKY
> I don't know what I'm doing.
> There wasn't a class on how to
> present a thesis.

> SAL
> Are you using rhetoric?

> VICKY
> No, what's that?

> SAL
> You do three things to make a
> case. I can teach you.

> VICKY
> I can't believe this, but yes.

Cornelius gets wheeled in accompanied by Keezheekoni. Sal and Vicky look at this, astonished and happy.

```
          INT. OLD FAITHFUL LODGE - CONFERENCE/RECOVERY ROOM - DAY
```

Medical personnel escort Cornelius into the room where
Pioneer rests. Dr. Young examines Cornelius as Julie
takes a pulse. Keezheekoni watches near the door, arms
folded.

>   DR. YOUNG
>   Get an IV stat. Electrolytes are
>   low.

Julie pulls over a drip line and grabs Cornelius' arm.

>   DR. YOUNG (CONT'D)
>   Muscle spasms. Luckily he didn't
>   have heart failure.

Julie pokes the line in his arm. Cornelius awakens.

>   DR. YOUNG (CONT'D)
>   Hello. I'm Dr. Young. What's your
>   name?

Sal and Vicky enter. Cornelius gathers everything in.

>   CORNELIUS
>   Cornelius.

>   DR. YOUNG
>   You're in a hospital now. How are
>   you feeling?

>   CORNELIUS
>   Not bad.
>   DR. YOUNG
>   You were in the woods awhile.

>   SAL
>   (coming in)
>   You did something many Americans
>   won't ever do, go without food
>   for a few days.

Cornelius turns his head and looks across the room. A
weak smile rises up the sides of his mouth.

                    CORNELIUS
          Sal!

                    SAL
          You're alive! Last time I saw
          you...

Sal's expression is relief and joy.

                    SAL (CONT'D)
          You lost a few pounds?

                    CORNELIUS
          I think I'll stay away from baked
          goods for a while.

                    PIONEER
          Stay away from my wife's sour-
          dough biscuits. So heavenly you
          have to hold 'em down with a
          fork.

Cornelius turns to Pioneer's bed.

                    CORNELIUS
          Pioneer!

                    PIONEER
          You look as surprised to see me
          as a summer snow.

                    CORNELIUS
          You okay?

                    PIONEER
          Never better. Finally got sober.

                    KEEZHEEKONI
          Abstinence is the cup from which
          gods drink.

                    PIONEER
          They like that better than beer?

A nurse comes in and whispers to Keezheekoni.

INT. OLD FAITHFUL LODGE OFFICE - DAY

In the main lobby, candlelights adorn wooden cross beams
and a Native American rug lays on the clean wooden
floor. The inner structure of this giant log cabin is an
intricate wooden skeleton.

Keezheekoni meets Kendall in a new, clean temporary office. Duka and Cody are no longer there.

> KENDALL
> Thanks for meeting me.

> KEEZHEEKONI
> What happens now?

> KENDALL
> I have a question to ask. If you
> were Park Superintendent what
> would you do?

> KEEZHEEKONI
> Did you know the two most painful
> things in life are being burned
> alive and giving childbirth?

> KENDALL
> You're talking about the park
> ranger that died and his widow.

> KEEZHEEKONI
> I'd want a full state funeral for
> Patrick with an honor guard and
> survivor benefits for the family.

> KENDALL
> Done.

> KEEZHEEKONI
> Then I'd re-open the park as a
> monument to the renewing power of
> nature.

                KENDALL
I'll let the press know. And how
about Pioneer? Duka said he had
been hanging around for months.
Said he may have even started one
of the fires.

                KEEZHEEKONI
I know Pioneer. He doesn't smoke
and he's harmless. I believe he'd
be a great person to do historic
reenactments for the park.

                KENDALL
Give a disabled Vet a job. Love
it.

                KEEZHEEKONI
And Duka?

                KENDALL
He's done here. He'll have to be
relocated.

                KEEZHEEKONI
How about a retirement place like
Phoenix? Maybe you can get him
something at the Grand Canyon?

                KENDALL
I can try. We need a temporary
Superintendent. How about it?

                KEEZHEEKONI
This place is a sacred land and
an important office.

                KENDALL
Begin immediately.

Kendall nods, smiles and they shake hands. Keezheekoni
takes out the white tribal choker from her pocket and
puts it on.

INT. UNIVERSITY OF MONTANA - CLASSROOM - DAY

Vicky presents her dissertation defense to the COMMIT-
TEE: three stuffy quasi-intellectual type PROFESSORS and
BULLOCK, all white men over 50.

> VICKY
> In conclusion, all the valuable
> minerals were locked up in the
> dead wood and now the post-fire
> soil's nutrient-rich.

Vicky hesitates and pauses to regain composure.

> VICKY
> All the measures of nitrogen,
> phosphorous, calcium, magnesium,
> and potassium were found to be at
> perfect levels and will allow
> healthy new vegetation to grow,
> which will in turn feed the vast
> Yellowstone wildlife population.
> We found millions of healthy
> lodgepole seeds spread over the
> forest floor and in many cases
> new trees already growing.

Vicky holds out her hands. There is something inside of
them. She opens them up and there sits the lodgepole
pinecone Sal gave her.

> VICKY (CONT'D)
> We hold the future of this forest
> in our hands.

There is a light clapping of hands. The men on the committee consult one another quickly. Heads nod.

> FORESTRY DEPARTMENT CHAIR
> Research was solid, all the data
> backed it up, we can feel your
> passion.

                    DEAN
          Hand us that dissertation paper.
          I think we can all sign the
          front.

Vicky hands over her paper.

                    COMMITTEE MEMBERS
          Congratulations, Dr. Iglesias.

                    DEAN
          Any plans to publish?

                    VICKY
          I'm sending it to a nationally
          syndicated top-tier journal.

                    DEAN
          And apply to the university for a
          professorship. We are getting rid
          of some deadwood.

He subconsciously glances sideways at Dr. Bullock.

                    DEAN (CONT'D)
          Commit four years and we can get
          your student loan forgiven.

Vicky raises her eyebrows.

EXT. YELLOWSTONE FOREST - NIGHT

On the forest floor, an innocent fawn sleeps peacefully
on a bed of pine needles under the trees. High in the
night sky, a halo surrounds the moon, a sign of oncoming
precipitation.

INT. VICKY'S HOUSE - NIGHT

In the living room, on a sofa, Vicky holds a glass of
wine. The two sit close together, turn toward one another. Scruffy sleeps near their feet.

Sal has the remote control and switches to the news
where a newscaster is in front of Lake Yellowstone.

                    ANN MARANEK (On TV)
          We're following an important news
          story in Yellowstone National
          Park.

EXT. YELLOWSTONE LAKE - VISTA POINT - DAY

Ann Maranek reports as the forest smolders in the background.

                    ANN MARANEK (CONT'D)
          The fires here were so intense
          they jumped several miles across
          Yellowstone Lake.

The TV displays a panoramic view of the lake and some
burning in the background. Rain falls. The newscaster
screams.

                    ANN MARANEK (CONT'D O.S.)
          But now it's raining! This dire
          situation may be over. At this
          very moment, you can hear the
          celebrations going on all over
          the park.

Camera pans to the forest beyond. Rain squelches the
fires in the trees and on the ground.

INT. VICKY'S HOUSE - NIGHT

Vicky turns an ear to the window.

                    VICKY
          Do you hear that? Rain!

                    SAL
          Nature's fire extinguisher.

                    VICKY
          This is great! Thanks for help-
          ing! I did it!

>   SAL
>   That helped me too. It taught me
>   that I can have value just by
>   helping others.

Sal moves his neck in a circle like a Michael Jackson
dance video.

>   SAL (CONT'D)
>   (Imitating Michael Jackson)
>   I've been lookin' at the man in
>   the mirror.

>   VICKY
>   Oh, God, don't. You're so bad.

Sal smiles. At least he got a reaction.

>   VICKY (CONT'D)
>   I was wondering something. What's
>   written on that paper in your
>   hat?

Sal grabs the paper from under the hat's brim.

>   SAL
>   Be honest. Signed Abe, the
>   fairest leader of them all.

Sal goes to put it away, but Vicky touches his arm. He
notices this and immediately stops.

>   SAL (CONT'D)
>   Oh yeah, I have a reminder to
>   tell Scruffy I never saw the
>   Broadway show *Cats*.

>   VICKY
>   You're making stuff up. Now for
>   real. Anything about me?
>   SAL
>   Hmm.

Sal looks at the paper. In the column for Vicky, there
is a long list of observations.

> VICKY
> What horrible things did you say?

SAL'S POV - "thin and fit with a great body" is crossed out. He looks down at the next line.

> SAL
> Smart. Knows a lot about nature.

> VICKY
> Interesting.

Vicky points her nose at the note and raises both her eyebrows.

> SAL
> Able to see the good in others.

> VICKY
> Awwww. Anything juicy?

She reaches over with a finger and touches his arm. Sal looks at her chewed-up cuticles.

> SAL
> Bites her nails.

> VICKY
> This whole thing was so nerve-wracking. Any more?

> SAL
> She's a challenge so game on.

Vicky bursts out laughing and spits out her drink.

> SAL (CONT'D)
> And can't handle her liquor.

Vicky takes a napkin and cleans up the wine. Sal grabs a napkin and helps.

> Vicky
> I haven't laughed like that since middle school.

                    SAL
          Wait, do you hear that?

There is a STRANGE NOISE outside.

                    VICKY
          That's elk. They're bugling.

                    SAL
          You just reminded me. The ram's
          horn. The shofar.

Sal grabs his wrist and looks down at it. There's no
watch.
                    SAL (CONT'D)
          What's today's date?

                    VICKY
          The twenty-first of September.

                    SAL
          Rosh Hashanah. The Jewish New
          Year!

                    VICKY
          Really? What do you usually do?

                    SAL
          Getting stuck in a fire counts as
          my penitence. I was going to make
          amends once I got back to New
          York. I'll miss the court date
          due to a force majeure.

                    VICKY
          Leave soon. By winter this place
          is only two miles from the North
          Pole.

                    SAL
          I'll go after the funeral.

Vicky smiles.

                    VICKY
        What do your impulses say now?

                    SAL
        I gave up impulses for the New
        Year.

Sal goes slowly in for a kiss. Vicky meets him halfway.

EXT. CHURCH - DAY

SUPER: CODY, WYOMING

Outside the church building, the flag is at half-mast
and an honor guard holds the doors open. As Park Service
employees enter, they take off their hats. Someone plays
the piano.

INT. CODY, WYOMING - CHURCH - DAY

In the main hall of the church, the seats face a pulpit.
A GIRL, 12, plays "Amazing Grace" on the piano. Duka,
Rick, Lily, Fire Lookout One, Jefferson, the smoke-
jumpers, Dr. Young, the Nurses and other Doctors, many
Firefighters, and Native Americans fill up the pews.

The Park Service Personnel are in uniform with a black
stripe placed horizontally across their badges or black
ribbons folded in loops and pinned above their nametags.
Red, Pipeman and Smokejumper One all bandaged.

In a pew, Pioneer wears a pressed military uniform. His
army hat is in his lap. He's shaved his beard and cut
his hair short and tight. His wife, DEBRA, sits close to
him and their two CHILDREN fidget beside them.

Secretary Kendall arrives dressed in a black tailored
suit and sits with Superintendent Keezheekoni, who wears
a black headband. Cornelius, a little thinner and more
confident, and Vicky arrive with Sal.
An easel on the stage holds a poster with pictures of
Patrick with his friends and family. A sign underneath
states, "Ranger - Husband - Father".

Two soldiers stand in front of the altar where a closed

casket lies on a wooden stand, surrounded by floral arrangements. In front, Maria sits mourning in black, the baby swaddled in her arms. Matt and Christine sit by her side.

Everyone quiets. CAMEAHWAIT, 60s, a Native American shaman and priest burns sagebrush in a shell and waves the smoke with an American bald eagle feather to the four corners of the room.

The music ends, and the soldiers present Maria with an immaculately folded American flag. Cameahwait puts the smoking shell onto a small table on the altar and steps up to the podium.

> CAMEAHWAIT
> Some say hell burns with the
> smell of sulfur and brimstone and
> Yellowstone is the Valley of the
> Shadow of Death. Some say, "This
> is the end!"

EXT. YELLOWSTONE PARK - FOREST - DAY

Black tree skeletons stand in the marred landscape like stark silhouettes under the steel blue of the heavens above.

> CAMEAHWAIT (CONT'D) (V.O.)
> They say the mighty trees have
> fallen and the towering forest is
> laid low. Yet, faithfully the
> forest regrows. From the tiny
> seeds of lodgepoles, baby pines
> burst through the blackened soil
> soon to be trees that are upright
> and straight; standing together,
> steady in the wind, faithful in
> yielding their fruit and life.

Under the fallen and burnt trees, numerous small pines burst through the blackened soil.

EXT. YELLOWSTONE PARK - HILLSIDE - DAY

Elk forage the hills on newly sprouted grasses and
sedges. One bugles.

                    CAMEAHWAIT (CONT'D) (V.O.)
              The animals live, protected in
              the wooden arc of the forest dur-
              ing this fiery flood.

EXT. YELLOWSTONE PARK - MEADOW - DAY

From blackened earth, vibrant flowers blossom through
the burnt soil.

                    CAMEAHWAIT (CONT'D V.O.)
              In truth, triumph follows this
              tragedy. Plants resume their ter-
              restrial kingdoms. Vibrant flow-
              ers now blossom from the black-
              ened earth. Brilliant red fire-
              weed shoots upward through the
              soil blooming in a garden of
              goldenrod and purple aster who
              praise the heavens.

INT. CODY, WYOMING - CHURCH - DAY

                    CAMEAHWAIT (CONT'D)
              We look up to those trees.
              They're our big brothers and big
              sisters, from the family tree of
              all life meaning we are not
              alone. The bodhi tree. Yggdrasil
              from Norse legends. The Garden of
              Eden had a tree with all the
              knowledge, the truth in you and
              in me. We craved it. "Take it,"
              we heard. We were selfish so the
              temptation was too much, and it
              was then we lost the battle with-
              in the landscape of our souls.

                    CONGREGATION
          Preach.

                    CAMEAHWAIT
          But within you is the seed of
          life, a kernel of goodness in
          your heart. Its husk cannot be
          destroyed. It will not be lost to
          fire, to impulse, to death. It
          grows compassion. Be patience in
          your nature, write tolerance in
          your soul, sow seeds of goodness
          in your mind, let this year's
          ring of growth be a true and
          faithful promise for compassion
          in your heart. Celebrate victory.
          Three people who were lost in the
          woods now are found!

                    CONGREGATION
          Amen!

Sal, Pioneer and Cornelius nod to one another.

                    CAMEAHWAIT
          Patrick is reborn of spirit. Our
          tears of sadness turn to joy! A
          child is born, a new life. Meet
          Alba!

                    CONGREGATION PERSON ONE
          Amen!

                    CONGREGATION PERSON TWO
          Hallelujah!

                    PIONEER
          Huzzah!

These rousing praises envelop Maria whose emotional love
focuses on the swaddled baby.

                    CAMEAHWAIT
          Just as the Easter Lily trumpets
          the floral beauty of spring, that
          love will be born unto this baby.

People shed the tears of bittersweet sadness and pose in
deep reflection. Cameahwait steps down to console Maria
as friends and family surround her and the sleeping
girl.

Dawn opens her eyes.

EXT. YELLOWSTONE PARK - DAY

Bison dot the Yellowstone plains beyond a winding and
silver river.

EXT. YELLOWSTONE FOREST - NIGHT

On the ground, baby lodgepole pines soak up water from
the wet soil under a waxing crescent moon.

Above, a rookery of crows caw in the trees. A nest is
tucked into the crook of a branch where a crow pecks at
Sal's watch.

In another nest, on another tree, another crow holds
Sal's belt pin in its beak like a celebratory cigar.

                                            FADE OUT

AFTERWORD

I witnessed the devastation from the 1988 Yellowstone fires in the fall of 1989. I saw firsthand that fire is a natural process for the regeneration of the lodgepole pine forest. This is when and where the concept for this story came to me. I thought, *"What better place for characters to go through the hell of rebirth than a burning forest unmarred by the hands of man?"*

The world's parks bless humanity and like all of them, Yellowstone is resplendent. As I hiked across a meadow, far away from everyone, I felt a natural and a divine energy. The trail ran across a flowered meadow. In the distance, a giant rock rested on a grassy hillside. The verdant green of trees on either side of the meadow vibrated under the brilliant blue sky. Yellowstone would make a great setting for a story. In this setting I would put the characters through hell and fire and fumaroles, lost and alone amid smell of brimstone. This resembled the picture of hell I have conceptualized from a young age.

I decided to tackle the problems that I and many other American's face: racism, working too much, inappropriate and unhealthy sexuality, overeating, and alcoholism. The five main male characters would each face one of these problems in their lives. I believe that in everyone there is good and everyone deserves a second chance, whether that is a religious rebirth, a mulligan on the golf course, or having to reboot your computer system. The characters are victorious witnesses to this belief.

Some people have abilities in music or math. I have an innate intelligence when it comes to understanding nature and having a connection to the higher power. I do not have great language skills and am not a born writer. I worked long and hard, over twenty years, editing this story. I wrote this as a movie script, as I have a visual mind and the terse form a screen-play works in favor of my strengths and weaknesses. I decided to write the story in the form of an allegory, since the story has religiously thematic undertones. I added numerous symbols to round the allegory out.

I have met and known many amazing people who inspired the development of the unique characters in the screenplay. I have never been in war, but even without any direct experience, I am not for war. Pioneer comes from this belief and from the fact my grandfather was an alcoholic. Sal is like so many guys I knew in college who were always partying and a lot of fun to be around. Cornelius is most like me. I love to eat and do not have six pack abs.

My mom was an architect in the early 70s. She worked too hard and yet was not taken seriously in the traditionally male dominated field of construction. Despite the prejudice against women in the workforce, she burned her bra and inspired her son.

The characters Keezheekoni and Vicky are heroes and like most women I have known, they are the key to this world getting us on a safe and calm path. They are my grandmother who gave me a second home. They are my mom who always believed in me. They are my aunt who made me feel valued. They are my cousin who is strong, honest, and true. They are my wife who gives me a love I never imagined possible. They are our daughters who will achieve a lot in this world. They are our co- workers and neighbors who contribute so much to our communities. It is for them and others like them that the heroes of this story are women.

This is not to discount the victories of the characters Sal, Pioneer, and Cornelius. They overcame the mental disease of addiction. Being sober is an achievement of a lifetime.

Lastly, though this story is based on actual events in Yellowstone National Park in September of 1988, it is a fictional account. Any depiction of rangers that is less than that of an extraordinary human being is unjust and unworthy of the people in this profession, who give their lives and serve for the public and the environment. I have always found them to be the best of people and not the type depicted here used for dramatic purposes.

ABOUT THE AUTHOR

Russ Brandon hails from Boxborough, Massachusetts, not where the Patriots play. He has been a teacher of exceptional children's for twenty-five years so one could say he is an exceptional children's teacher, but let's just say he works hard and really cares about helping the children learn. He has a close affinity to nature, is a proponent of Adler's philosophy and Buddha's Dharma. Though he grew up with cats, he has a heartfelt love for dogs. In the summer time, after gardening, landscaping and working the lawn, he writes screenplays.

Holy Smoke: Trapped by Hellfire is an official selection of fifteen screenplay competitions world- wide. Russ Brandon is the author of numerous other short movie and television scripts which have been included in forty writing and film competitions, mostly throughout the US. Several of these are movies that have been screened from North Carolina to California and Jamaica to Rio de Janeiro.

Ten percent of all proceeds from the sale of this story will be donated to organizations helping stem racism and prejudice within our world. Look on the Holy Smoke; Trapped by Hellfire Facebook page for an upcoming survey in which you can suggest a worthy charity.

Made in the USA
Columbia, SC
20 June 2021